Getting Started as a
Pharmacy
Manager

Notice

The author, editor, and publisher have made every effort to ensure the accuracy and completeness of the information presented in this book. However, the author, editor, and publisher cannot be held responsible for the continued currency of the information, any inadvertent errors or omissions, or the application of this information. Therefore, the author, editor, and publisher shall have no liability to any person or entity with regard to claims, loss, or damage caused or alleged to be caused, directly or indirectly, by the use of information contained herein.

Getting Started as a
Pharmacy
Manager

Lynette R. Bradley-Baker, BSPharm, PhD

Director of Professional Alliance Development
American Association of Colleges of Pharmacy
Alexandria, Virginia

American Pharmacists Association®
Improving medication use. Advancing patient care.

APhA   **Washington, D.C.**

Managing and Content Editor: Vicki Meade, Meade Communications
Acquiring Editor: Sandra Cannon
Proofreader: Betty Bruner
Indexer: Jennifer Burton, Columbia Indexing Group
Cover Designer: Scott Neitzke, APhA Creative Services
Layout and Graphics: Michele A. Danoff, Graphics by Design

© 2012 by the American Pharmacists Association
APhA was founded in 1852 as the American Pharmaceutical Association.

Published by the American Pharmacists Association
2215 Constitution Avenue, N.W.
Washington, DC 20037-2985
www.pharmacist.com
www.pharmacylibrary.com

To comment on this book via email, send your message to the publisher at
aphabooks@aphanet.org

Library of Congress Cataloging-in-Publication Data

Bradley-Baker, Lynette R.
  Getting started as a pharmacy manager / Lynette R. Bradley-Baker.
    p. ; cm.
  Includes bibliographical references and index.
  ISBN 978-1-58212-154-3
  I. American Pharmacists Association. II. Title.
  [DNLM: 1. Pharmacy Administration. 2. Pharmacists—Organization &
  administration. QV 737]

  615.1068—dc23
                        2011042344

How to Order This Book

Online: www.pharmacist.com/shop_apha
By phone: 800-878-0729 (from the United States and Canada)
VISA®, MasterCard®, and American Express® cards accepted

Dedication

To three of the best managers I have learned from:
My husband, Troy Baker; my mother, Vivian Bradley;
and my father, Leroy Bradley—a retired pharmacist who
worked in management roles throughout his 43-year career.

Thank you all so much for the support and love you've
given me for my personal and professional pursuits.

Contents

Preface

Congratulations! You're a pharmacy manager—or are headed in that direction. This book is designed to help you make the transition from student or staff pharmacist to manager. It's an exciting time for you, but you may feel some anxiety, too, which this book can assuage by supplying practical knowledge for success.

Pharmacy managers fill a multidimensional role and handle responsibilities that ultimately affect patient outcomes. Legal, ethical, operational, human resources, and financial issues as well as professional and competency requirements all fall under the manager's umbrella, regardless of practice setting. Managers must understand and apply tools and information to create an efficient, comfortable, and patient-oriented pharmacy setting.

Getting Started as a Pharmacy Manager was written as an easy, concise resource to help you quickly grasp important information. Chapters cover key aspects of pharmacy management related to business, processes, and people. Each chapter also contains:

- "Words of wisdom" in question-and-answer format from pharmacy managers in a variety of pharmacy practice settings.

- Tables and sidebars with concise tips.

- Listings of resources for additional information.

- Exercises that help you explore topics covered in the chapter.

I would have been very grateful for a reference like this as I embarked on my professional pharmacy career. I moved from community (retail) pharmacy practice to research, academia, and pharmacy association management, and I've continuously used the principles discussed in this book as I work toward being the most efficient and effective pharmacy professional possible. It's an exciting journey and I look forward to the challenges and opportunities ahead.

I'm grateful to the pharmacy managers who supplied interviews for the book, sharing their stories and advice. They have different levels of management experience; some are very early in their careers as managers while others have been in practice for over 20 years. I hope their information gives you useful insights to prepare you for and help you maintain a successful career in pharmacy management.

Best of luck as you move ahead. Learning the ropes as a pharmacy manager may be frustrating at times, but as you go through ups and downs, things will fall into place, your knowledge and confidence will grow, and you'll find yourself developing into a solid, successful professional.

Lynette R. Bradley-Baker
November 2011

Acknowledgments

This book would not have been possible without the inspiration, constructive criticism, and guidance I have received from managers, supervisors, and pharmacists throughout my career.

In addition, the following pharmacists committed time and resources to contribute to this book, and I thank them for sharing their experience and advice with aspiring pharmacy managers.

Jennifer Brandt, PharmD

Brian Ellsworth, PharmD

Lenna Israbian-Jamgochian, PharmD

DeAnna (Dixie) Leikach, RPh, MBA Candidate

Craig Long, PharmD

Eileen Munch, PharmD

Matthew Shimoda, PharmD

Meghan Sullivan, PharmD

Marc Summerfield, RPh, MS

Janet Teeters, RPh, MS

Chapter 1

The Basics of Pharmacy Management

Definition of a Pharmacy Manager

If you're reading this book, most likely you're an aspiring pharmacy manager or fairly new to the role. What, in a nutshell, do pharmacy managers do?

Regardless of the setting, a pharmacy manager plans, directs, and monitors pharmacy operations and the work of employees. Responsibilities may include hiring, promoting, and terminating employees as well as delegating duties and responsibilities to employees and taking corrective action, if necessary. Several factors determine how many people report to the pharmacy manager, but the primary driver is the number and complexity of the pharmacy team's responsibilities. Pharmacy managers also ensure adherence to applicable state and federal laws and regulations.

An example of a job description for a pharmacy manager appears in Figure 1-1, on page 2. Before stepping into a pharmacy manager role, you should be given a job description so you're clear about your level of responsibility.

Pharmacy managers serve a multifaceted role, which involves both operating the pharmacy and managing people who work there. This chapter gives you an overview of the following:

- Roles and responsibilities of a pharmacy manager

- Managing teams

- Management styles

- Valuing diversity

- Communicating with success

Figure 1-1 | **Example of a Pharmacy Manager Job Description**

Summary: The Pharmacy Manager supervises the daily operations of the Pharmacy Department and works with the Pharmacy Supervisor to accomplish the goals and objectives for the pharmacy.

Responsibilities:
- Maintain clinical competency and function in patient care activities 50-80% of their time

- Develop and maintain department policies and procedures, goals, objectives, quality assurance programs, safety, and environmental and infection control standards

- Manage the appropriate purchasing, control, and security of all drug products and medical supplies

- Respond to any concerns, including complaints, errors, reactions, and safety procedures, that are brought forth by pharmacy customers, health care providers, and pharmacy employees

- Hire and ensure proper training for all new pharmacy employees

- Prepare employee work schedules, evaluate employee work performance, and make recommendations for all pharmacy personnel actions

- Attend all meetings as required for pharmacy management members

Minimum Qualifications:
- Doctor of Pharmacy degree or Bachelor of Science degree in Pharmacy

- A minimum of five years of staff pharmacist experience in this practice setting

- Current pharmacist license in this state

- Excellent communication skills, flexibility, and ability to work as part of a team

- Self-directed with excellent time management skills and able to work independently

Relationships and Expectations

Although the definition of a pharmacy manager's role may sound simple, the reality is much more complex and involves multidimensional relationships. Figure 1-2 gives a sense of the relationships a pharmacy manager must maintain.

Figure 1-2 | **Roles of a Pharmacy Manager**

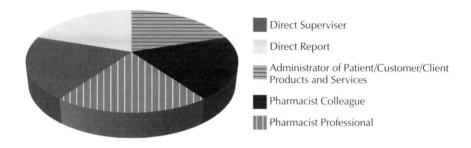

Direct Superviser
Direct Report
Administrator of Patient/Customer/Client Products and Services
Pharmacist Colleague
Pharmacist Professional

To further elaborate on the pie chart in Figure 1-2, the pharmacy manager fulfills these roles:

- **Direct Supervisor** – overseeing other personnel such as pharmacy technicians, student pharmacists or pharmacy interns, and both nonlicensed and registered pharmacy personnel in the pharmacy.

- **Direct Report** – reporting up to someone else, such as a middle or senior manager or the pharmacy owner. The pharmacy manager may also interact with other senior management members.

- **Administrator of Patient, Customer, or Client Services** – ensuring that the products and services needed by the targeted patient, customer, or client groups are available and maintained. As an administrator, a pharmacy manager has to interact and communicate with people on the receiving end of these services as well as those who can assist in providing these services, such as wholesale distributors and suppliers.

- **Colleague to Other Pharmacists** – participating as a member of a group of pharmacist professionals who may be consulted for mentoring, training, education, or advice.

- **Pharmacist Professional** – living up to the responsibilities that come with the formal education and training of a professional pharmacist, such as maintaining licensure and staying competent to ensure that mandated services are diligently performed.

Table 1-1 details some responsibilities and expectations of pharmacy managers.

Table 1-1 | **Responsibilities and Expectations of the Pharmacy Manager**

Pharmacy Manager Role	Expectations
Direct Supervisor	1. Communicate and direct the pharmacy's goals. 2. Support direct reports as they accomplish tasks, including offering guidance, resources, training, and a listening ear. 3. Develop and nurture an environment that will help direct reports succeed. 4. Solve problems and answer questions quickly and accurately. 5. Represent the views of your team to others, both inside and outside of the organization.
Direct Report	1. Accept accountability for the pharmacy operations. 2. Motivate direct reports to support organizational goals and initiatives. 3. Formulate and follow up on pharmacy plans. 4. Balance the group's interests with those of others. 5. Protect the reputations of superiors and of the company.
Administrator of Patient Products and Services	1. Represent the pharmacy. 2. Accept accountability for the pharmacy's ability or inability to provide products and services. 3. Provide methods or plans to ensure that products and services are available for acceptance, integration, and delivery. 4. Do what is best for the patient, customer, or client.
Colleague to Other Pharmacists	1. Represent the pharmacy. 2. Share needed information and resources. 3. Set agendas and build networks. 4. Treat peers as partners. 5. Do what is best for the organization and profession.

It Takes a Team

To carry out your responsibilities and achieve your desired outcomes as a pharmacy manager, you need an effective team in place. You're no longer responsible only for your individual goals; now you need to lead other people. No single person can accomplish everything that has to be done in the pharmacy.

To achieve your given responsibilities, your key efforts will fall into these categories:

- Setting the agenda

- Building a team and network

- Managing teams

- Assessing goals

Setting the Agenda

The pharmacy manager sets the agenda for the pharmacy—that is, the overall plan that allows the pharmacy to meet important goals. Often, the pharmacy manager's supervisor is the one who hands down the goals that need to be met, including the following:

- Financial—budget, payroll, etc.

- Patient/customer—satisfaction, utilization of pharmacy services, etc.

- Pharmacy personnel—training, professional and skill development, etc.

In setting the agenda, your challenge is to develop and articulate strategies that will help your team support the company's objectives and to ensure that those strategies are implemented.[1] To be an agenda setter, pharmacy managers must:

The Pharmacy Manager— Making it Simple

Just as becoming a pharmacist takes commitment and hard work, so does becoming an effective pharmacy manager. The basics include:

- Define the pharmacy manager's roles and how these roles play out in your multiple relationships.

- Develop the steps needed to achieve the responsibilities and goals of a pharmacy manager.

- Demonstrate the ability to employ an appropriate management or leadership style, depending on the situation.

- Communicate, both orally and in writing, to all those who contribute to the pharmacy's operations and management.

- Recognize the value of diversity and its role in managing the pharmacy.

- View themselves as an entrepreneur running their own business and address all the forces that may make or break their business.

- Expand their perspective to include not only their pharmacy team, but also the larger organization, as well as the industry and business environment in which their pharmacy operates.

- Maintain a budget to support their agenda—which may involve developing the budget, too, depending on their pharmacy.

- Balance any tensions between their team and other groups or the larger organization, including clarifying priorities and making mutually acceptable compromises.

- Accept that the identified priorities may not necessarily be shared by direct reports unless the pharmacy manager communicates his or her vision.

Agenda setting is a complex process of thought and decision-making that allows the pharmacy manager to take into account multiple factors beyond your individual pharmacy team. Often, you have to depend on additional networks of both personal and professional contacts, which you must develop and nurture.

Building a Team and Network

As a pharmacy manager, you'll spend the majority of your waking hours with your pharmacy team members—even more than you typically spend with your family. The manager is at the apex of three critical relationships in the work environment:[2]

1. Manager–Individual Team Member

2. Manager–Pharmacy Team

3. Pharmacy Team–Individual Team Member

Each team member has unique needs, motivations, and style of communication. If you have good communication with individual team members, each person is more likely to work cohesively as a group. You will better understand individual strengths and challenges and those of the team as a whole, and you are better able to influence how each team member relates to the others.

Building a network involves strengthening and sustaining mutually beneficial relationships with everyone you interact with: supervisors, peers, direct reports, patients, clients, suppliers, and people from partnering organizations, such as physician groups. To be effective in your efforts, you must:

> A pharmacy manager plans, directs, and monitors pharmacy operations and the work of employees.

- View yourself as a "people developer" and not a "task doer."

- Recognize the value in organizational politics of sharing and forming alliances.

- Understand where you fit in the total organization and how to use your position and personal qualities to achieve your goals and get needed resources—as well as how to help others do the same.

- Recognize the importance of developing relationships with people outside as well as inside your pharmacy team.

- Be open to creating opportunities to spend time with your supervisors, peers, and direct reports—such as lunches, meetings, and social events.

- Be willing to be an active participant in your pharmacy and organization to build up your reputation and that of your pharmacy group.

Establishing networks can be challenging and it takes time, because you must build trust with others and demonstrate your competence and professionalism. Keep the following in mind:

- Personal success will be defined by how well the pharmacy team achieves its objectives.

- As a pharmacy manager, your success will also be defined by how much you've helped direct reports develop their skill set.

- You may need to ask others for assistance in developing your team's skills and your own management skills.

Managing Teams

In most pharmacy settings, working well as a team is paramount. A pharmacy team brings a combination of knowledge, expertise, and perspective that one person cannot contribute alone. An effective team can deliver the following productive results:

- Increased performance and creativity by focusing the team members' talents on a specific task, duty, or challenge.

- Ability to delegate effectively and have flexibility in assigning tasks.

- Improved communication.

- Effective cross-training so multiple team members can contribute to specialized tasks and assignments.

- Smooth implementation resulting from a team that shares commitment and responsibilities.

Finding Balance Among Continua

To manage any kind of team—whether in pharmacy or elsewhere—you have to lead the team, which requires you to adapt your managerial style to fit the characteristics of various team members and pharmacy situations. Figure 1-3 shows the four examples of the "team leadership continua" along which managers can move as necessary.

Figure 1-3 | The Four Continua of Team Leadership

1.	Embrace individual differences ←..............→	Embrace group identity and goals
2.	Foster support among team members ←..............→	Foster confrontation among team members
3.	Focus on current team performance ←..............→	Focus on team learning and development
4.	Emphasize managerial authority ←..............→	Emphasize team members' discretion and autonomy

Source: Adapted from Harvard Business School ManageMentor PLUS online program. *Becoming a Manager.* Boston: Harvard Business School Publishing; 2009.

Each continuum shows a pair of conflicting forces that lie at the heart of every team. Sometimes it is appropriate to gravitate toward one polar end or the other, while at other times it works best to settle somewhere in the middle. Where you concentrate along each continuum depends on the skills, knowledge, and commitment of your team members, the performance of the team and the pharmacy, and your style as a manager.

Refrain from spending too much time at either end of a continuum because the team's performance may suffer. Table 1-2 has examples of how a pharmacy manager may spend too much time along a continuum and what can be done to prevent it. Finding the right balance along any of the four team-leadership continua may be a challenge, but it is worth the effort in order to build an effective, flexible, and innovative team that can adapt to changes and challenges that will arise in pharmacy practice.

Table 1-2 | **Imbalances to Avoid in the Team Leadership Continua**

Example of Management Imbalance	Potential Consequence	Pharmacy Manager Challenge
Overemphasizing individual differences within the pharmacy team	Team members may become overly competitive, engage in disruptive conflicts, and develop a "win/lose" mind-set.	Allow individual differences and freedom, but establish goals and an agenda to which all team members are committed.
Overemphasizing support within the pharmacy team	Team members avoid healthy, productive confrontation and suppress their thoughts and feelings to promote harmony.	Find ways to encourage team members to express conflicting thoughts and ideas without letting disagreements become personal or disruptive.
Overemphasizing the pharmacy team's current performance	Team focuses on short-term results and doesn't develop the learning capacities it needs to take on new challenges and be innovative in the long term.	Treat mistakes as sources of learning rather than reasons for punishment. Encourage risk-taking.
Overemphasizing managerial authority	Team members don't have the opportunity to develop their own decision-making and critical-thinking skills.	Decide when to make a decision alone, when to make a decision jointly with another team member, and when to ask for consensus or delegate the decision.

Source: Adapted from Harvard Business School ManageMentor PLUS online program. *Becoming a Manager.* Boston: Harvard Business School Publishing; 2009.

Managerial Styles

Table 1-3 describes four typical managerial styles and gives examples of situations in which each style is useful. Often, you have to adjust your management style based on the situation and the people with whom you are interacting.

Table 1-3 | Typical Managerial Styles

Managerial Style	Description of Style	Example of When to Use the Style
Directive or Autocratic	Monitoring a team member closely and providing more explicit instructions and demands.	A pharmacy team member taking a new responsibility (i.e., monitoring pharmacy).
Coaching or Paternalistic	Working with a team member to resolve a concern or issue.	Discussion with a pharmacy team member who feels resentful because he or she was not selected for a new responsibility, to illuminate why the member was not selected for the task (i.e., what skills need to be developed).
Supportive or Democratic	Encouraging a team member to identify strengths and build upon them (so as to gradually take on more tasks and risks).	Working with a pharmacy team member who has been given a new responsibility by providing individualized instruction and continuous feedback.
Delegating or Laissez-faire	Providing a team member with the autonomy and trust with key responsibilities and decision making.	Providing more respon-sibilities to the pharmacy team member who monitors pharmacy inventory.

Source: Adapted from Harvard Business School ManageMentor PLUS online program. *Becoming a Manager.* Boston: Harvard Business School Publishing; 2009.

To adapt your style effectively, you must assess what each team member needs—which involves observing and grasping the individual's

> You must adapt your managerial style to fit the charac- teristics of various team members and pharmacy situations.

- Capabilities

- Level of commitment

- Desire for professional development

Over time, team members will accept and trust your versatility as a manager.

Assessing Goals

Before you became a pharmacy manager, you probably defined success in terms of your individual performance. But now your responsibility is to get things accomplished through other people. Success will be measured differently and will be determined by setting goals.

Goal setting is a formal process in which you define targets for the pharmacy to achieve. Setting solid goals creates a long-term vision for a pharmacy and helps motivate personnel to achieve that vision.

- Goals can have different time frames and levels of importance.

- Short-term goals can be accomplished in one or two months.

- Long-term goals are achieved over the course of several months, a year, or several years.

In terms of importance, goals are usually classified into one of the following categories:[2]

- Critical: Goals essential for the pharmacy to continue operating successfully. An example would be a specific percentage of medications processed with a generic equivalent or a lower-cost therapeutically equivalent alternative.

- Solution-oriented: Goals helping to provide a more desirable business condition or to take advantage of a business opportunity.

An example would be establishing a specific number of pharmacist-administered immunizations for the pharmacy to provide.

- Nice-to-have: Goals that make improvements to enhance business. Such goals usually relate to making activities faster or easier. An example would be creating a loyalty program for patrons of a pharmacy or a pharmacy program designed to help asthma patients adhere to their medication regimens.

Pharmacy managers should set both individual goals and goals for the pharmacy team. Among the goals you set may be pharmacy goals requiring specific skills that cannot be delegated to one member of the team, as well as goals that reflect the pharmacy manager's contributions to team members' goals—such as providing individualized training so a team member can take the test to become a nationally certified pharmacy technician.

Table 1-4 lists the steps you should follow to set goals—both individual and team-based—so that their success can be measured. Your success as a pharmacy manager will be defined by:

- How well your pharmacy team achieves its objectives.

- How much you have helped your team members develop their skills and manage tasks effectively.

- How strongly your team's achievements have supported the pharmacy's or company's objectives and strategies.

You may feel disheartened at first to know that your individual success is strongly correlated with that of your team, but as you grow in the manager role, you will feel rewarded from different sources than you have in the past. Many pharmacy managers learn to enjoy helping other people develop and succeed, discovering that they can be effective coaches who bring out the talent in others and gaining satisfaction from adapting to their new role and mastering new responsibilities.

Table 1-4 | Steps for Setting Goals

Step	Issues for Consideration
Identify potential goals	This should be done once or twice a year.
Prioritize and select goals	Identify criteria for prioritizing goals. Review the list of goals and rank their priority—typically in terms of their value and importance.
Write out goals	Create a detailed, written description of each goal, using SMART criteria as a guideline: Specific: the goal can be described in detail. Measurable: the goal is able to be measured using either quantitative or qualitative assessments. Achievable: the goal is not lofty or unattainable. Realistic: the goal can be accomplished given existing constraints, such as time and resources. Timely: the goal can be achieved within a specified time frame.
Plan how to achieve goals	Identify a strategy and tactics that will assist in reaching the goal. Include considerations such as resources and methods to combat potential obstacles. Establish milestones and time frames.
Pursue goals, while monitoring progress along the way	As progress is made toward the goal, update all parties involved in achieving it. Reassess the strategy or tactics and restructure if necessary.
Evaluate the goals	Periodically assess whether the goals are still realistic, timely, and relevant. You may need to revise the goal, which requires communication and buy-in from involved parties. When a goal is reached, confirm that others agree that the desired impact has been achieved.

Diversity and Team Culture in Management

Understanding diversity is a very important part of management in any organization. Many people think of "diversity" as issues related to race or gender, but in the workplace, diversity involves all kinds of differences, as shown in Tables 1-5 and 1-6. These differences may influence pharmacy team members' needs, their ways of communicating and interacting, and their priorities. Misunderstanding and other difficulties can arise, but diversity also is a source of special contributions each person brings to the pharmacy team.

Table 1-5 | Workplace Diversity Attributes

Diversity Attribute	Description
Tenure	Some people may be in high school or college, while others may have more experience.
Cultural background	People may come from different regions of the country or from other countries outside the United States.
Physical ability	People may use various forms of assistive technologies, such as wheelchairs, to perform their work.
Working or learning style	People may approach a task in different ways. Some may approach it logically and methodically, while others are more intuitive and creative.
Professional motivations	People differ in what they would like to pursue in their career. Some may have the goal of a management position; others are satisfied serving as an individual contributor.
Management preferences	People may want more direction and contact from their manager and others may not.
Experience level	People have multiple levels of experience in performing the tasks that make up their jobs as a result of their work history, training, and education, both formal and informal.

Source: Adapted from National Oceanographic and Atmospheric Association Office of Diversity. Tips to Improve Interaction and Communication Among the Generations. http://honolulu.hawaii. edu/intranet/committees/FacDevCom/guidebk/teachtip/intergencomm.htm. Accessed April 25, 2011.

Table 1-6 | Generational Considerations

	Generations (based on year of birth)			
	Generation Y (born 1978-1995)	Generation X (born 1966-1977)	Baby Boomers (born 1947-1965)	Traditionalist (born before 1946)
Common Motivators	Positive Reinforcement	Entrepreneurial Spirit	Competition	Private
	Autonomy	Independent	Teamwork	Hard Workers
	Positive Attitude	Continuous Feedback	Success Driven	Respect for Authority
	Diversity	Creative	Hard Workers	Trustworthy
	Technology	Loyalty	Dedicated to a Cause	Social Order
Communication Considerations	Create a fun, learning work environment	Use email	Recognize that how they are approached (verbal and body language) is important to them	They are private, so don't expect active sharing of their thoughts
	Ask them for feedback and provide them with constant feedback	Provide regular feedback and share information regularly	Use an open, direct style	Face-to-face or written (not necessarily email) communication is preferred
	Encourage them to take risks	Use informal communication styles	Answer their questions thoroughly	Their time is important—have a purpose and don't waste their time

Source: Adapted from National Oceanographic and Atmospheric Association Office of Diversity. Tips to Improve Interaction and Communication Among the Generations. http://honolulu.hawaii. edu/intranet/committees/FacDevCom/guidebk/teachtip/intergencomm.htm. Accessed April 25, 2011.

Each pharmacy team has it own culture, which defines its distinct way of:

- Solving problems and meeting challenges.

- Getting work completed.

- Communicating.

- Learning.

- Dealing with conflict.

- Interacting with patients and other external team members.

Useful Attributes of a Manager

Some of the attributes below may take longer to achieve than others, but all are important to strive for as you transition into a pharmacy manager position.

Maintains self-control. You can be counted on to behave maturely and appropriately according to the situation.

Always is fair to everyone. You delegate work assignments fairly, consistently enforce policies and procedures, and avoid favoritism.

Never is afraid to say "I don't know" or "I made a mistake." No one knows everything, and people respect when someone says so. The key is to utilize resources and networks to find the correct answer and communicate it back to everyone who needs to know.

Attentively listens. It is one thing to hear what someone is saying and quite another to actively listen to what a person is saying, asking, or trying to communicate.

Gains people's trust. Once a manager has someone's trust, it is hard to lose it. With your direct reports, maintaining trust includes being willing to represent your team to higher management.

Encourages communication. Building a team environment includes both one-way and multidimensional communication.

Realizes the importance of understanding the technological knowledge of the work being supervised. You must know the most efficient methods of operating a pharmacy so you can be an effective coach, teacher, and evaluator of your staff.

- Marking successes and dealing with disappointments.

A team's culture will have developed, in part, from the group members' special and different characteristics, including diversity characteristics. In addition, the team's culture may have been shaped by the former pharmacy manager's style and expectations.

> Diversity is a source of special contributions each person brings to the pharmacy team.

To build effective relationships with new direct reports, don't try to make improvements too soon. Consider the following points:

- Avoid predetermined assumptions about a pharmacy team.

- Learn about the diversity of pharmacy team members, outside of physical attributes, by talking with them and observing them in action.

- Decide how best to treat each member fairly to assist him or her to succeed.

Avoid Assumptions

When first meeting a pharmacy team that is already in place, do not assume that everyone on the team is similar and can be "molded" into what you want. To get to know pharmacy team members better, you have to talk with them, ask questions, and observe them. Your ultimate goal is to understand what motivates each team member, how he or she deals with conflict, and how each member prefers to be managed.

Be Fair

Fairness is an important concept for managers to grasp. Fair treatment does not mean identical or equal treatment; instead it means finding the best ways to help each team member succeed—approaches that may be different based on each person's diversity-related aspects.

Understanding and adapting to a team's diversity, whether you inherit the team or new members join along the way, is an important part of shaping the team and guiding it toward success. Your skills in this area also help identify you as a team leader and motivator.

Communicating with Success

Being able to communicate effectively is an indispensable skill for any manager. The extended role of the pharmacist necessitates spending a great amount of time talking with people, including physicians, patients, and pharmacy team members.[3] Every aspect of the pharmacy manager's daily activities involves communication, including:

- Patient counseling and education.

- Discussions with middle and senior management or the pharmacy owner.

- Consultations and interactions with other health care providers.

- Interviewing potential candidates for the pharmacy team.

- Coaching, counseling, and delegating to pharmacy team members.

The purpose of communication is not just to deliver a message to the recipient, but to influence or bring about a change in that person's knowledge, attitudes, or behavior.[4] Effective communication must be a two-way process between the sender of the message and the receiver; if the person receiving the message doesn't understand it, communication fails. The receiver should be able to ask questions of the sender, and the sender should take the time to ask questions of the receiver to ensure that the intended message was delivered.

Table 1-7 lists aspects of communication you need to consider when delivering and receiving information in your many relationships. You must train yourself to observe the reactions of people you are communicating with—whether you are interacting in person or some other way, such as telephone or email—to ensure that your message is being received and understood.

You also must become aware of any tendencies you have that could interfere with good communication and cause messages to be misunderstood. For example, you may have extensive clinical knowledge about a disease state and its treatment and be eager to share this information with your patients, but if you concentrate only on providing the information and don't take time to answer questions or you fail to watch for signs that the patient doesn't understand such as a blank stare or lack of eye contact—your efforts will not be successful.

Table 1-7 | Aspects of Communication

Aspect	Additional Considerations
Tone of Speech	The tone of a message often influences whether the receiver is going to listen and therefore whether the message is received. For example, a whining tone may elicit a different response than a friendly tone.
Accent	In today's society, you encounter many different accents. Some people may have to listen closer and harder when communicating with those who have accents.
Listening and Questioning Skills	This involves hearing the message, asking questions regarding the message, and observing during the communication process. Ask open-ended questions when possible—those that can't be answered with a simple "yes" or "no"—to ensure that the message is understood. Also, pay attention to body language, facial expressions, gestures, and eye contact.
Body Language	A person's body language conveys to others his or her approachability and receptivity to viewpoints and opinions. Body language includes gestures, facial expression, eye contact, physical contact, body posture, body space, and proximity to other people.

Clear verbal and nonverbal communication is critical for pharmacy managers. In addition to using language that is easy to understand and avoiding overloading patients with too much information, you often need to repeat key messages to ensure that the most important points stick in the listener's mind. For example, when talking with patients about medications, if they seem confused or are unable to repeat instructions back to you, you need to restate the information in different words and verify that they comprehend. Knowing how to clarify issues without using emotion is valuable for managers—especially in conflict situations, which will be discussed in Chapter 3.

Pharmacy managers work in an environment with many potential barriers to effective communication and must constantly assess their skills.

Brian Ellsworth, PharmD

Pharmacy Team Leader
CVS Pharmacy

Q: Talk a little about your professional background.

I graduated from the University of Maryland School of Pharmacy in May 2010, receiving a Doctor of Pharmacy degree. I've worked for CVS Pharmacy since 2004 and signed with the company as a pharmacy team leader upon my graduation. I'm certified as a provider of both cardiopulmonary resuscitation and immunizations. My affiliations include the American Pharmacists Association, Maryland Pharmacists Association, Kappa Psi Pharmaceutical Fraternity, and Phi Lambda Sigma Leadership Fraternity.

Q: What advice would you give to a student or staff pharmacist with the goal of being a pharmacy manager?

Take time to understand the business. Successful pharmacy managers know how the business runs and what makes it more efficient; they become a student of the business. Because pharmacy is much more than filling prescriptions, the pharmacy manager should be able to identify what makes the business flourish and know how to execute these activities.

Q: What prepared you to take a pharmacy manager position?

My experience with the company played an essential role. I was always curious to know why we did things they way we did and how we could do them better. I took the time to ask questions and learn about the business. I also have a strong desire to challenge myself; I wanted to work in a pharmacy that had several opportunities to improve—and to take advantage of those opportunities.

Q: What challenges did you face as a new pharmacy manager?

Although I had experience with the company, I did not have experience being a pharmacist, so my most important challenge was learning how to balance best practice with running a business.

With most of my technicians close to my age or older, I faced interpersonal challenges. As the pharmacy manager, your staff has to respect you as a leader and respond accordingly to the challenges, praise, and criticism you present to them.

Q: What benefits and rewards have you experienced as a new pharmacy manager?

Being a pharmacy manager has been a great experience thus far. I've grown tremendously as a person and professional. I enjoy being the face of the pharmacy and have no problem accepting responsibility for anything that takes place at the pharmacy. I'm thankful to be in this position, as it's the first step in further advancing my career. Knowing how to resolve conflicts is a key skill for successful pharmacy managers and is useful in both professional and personal life.

Q: What role has networking, having a mentor, or involvement in profes-sional associations had in your development as a pharmacy manager?

It is very refreshing to know that I am not alone in being a pharmacy manager. I had mentors every step of the way and absorbed as much information as I could from them. I studied everything they did, every managerial decision they made. Networking and professional associations have also been essential as I can share my experiences and get opinions and advice from my peers.

Q: From your perspective, what are the attributes of a manager? Of a leader?

I believe managers and leaders share numerous attributes. They need to be able to solve problems under pressure while ensuring they are making sound business decisions. They need to be innovative, always finding ways to advance the practice and profession. Managers and leaders must be patient; the world cannot be changed overnight. It is very important to set goals; however, those goals must be realistic and given the proper time to be achieved.

Managers and leaders must understand that criticism will be given to them, whether they were involved in a situation or not. They must be prepared to pass on praise to others, because teamwork is essential to suc-cess. In working with a team, a manager or leader must be able to delegate tasks. You get greater productivity, efficiency, and engagement when you involve the whole team rather than trying to take on everything alone.

Dixie Leikach, RPh

Owner and Vice President
Finksburg Pharmacy, Finksburg, Maryland

Q: Talk a little about your professional background.

My pharmacy career began in Salisbury, Maryland, when I was working at a local ice cream store and the pharmacist of the Rite Aid in the shopping center came in wearing her nametag. I started a conversation and said I was planning on going to pharmacy school. By chance, the position of pharmacy technician was available. I applied the next day and began the first step in my career.

I graduated from the University of Maryland School of Pharmacy in 1992 and continued working for Rite Aid throughout school. This career path continued and my supervisor, Harold Holmes, taught me everything he knew. After my pharmacist licensure, Harold promoted me to the position of pharmacy manager and "base store" coordinator for all of his stores. Through restructuring and the birth of our two sons, Eric and Marc, I spent many years in a part-time pharmacist position without the title of pharmacy manager.

I stayed involved in the profession in many ways. I was a member of the Maryland Pharmacists Association's Board of Trustees and of the Maryland Continuing Education Coordinating Council, and I was on the Grand Council for Lambda Kappa Sigma, International Pharmacy Fraternity. I also explored many volunteer opportunities at The Associated: Jewish Community Federation of Baltimore.

Q: What path did your career take?

My husband, Neil, and I opened our first independent pharmacy in February 1999 in Catonsville, Maryland. At this time, I went back to work full-time for NeighborCare and became the pharmacy manager. My career there continued until we opened our second pharmacy in October 2003 in Finksburg, Maryland. This is the location that I currently manage, with a staff of six employees. The Catonsville location is now separated into a retail location and a closed-door location for assisted living home and group home business.

Q: What advice do you have for aspiring pharmacy managers?

A pharmacist sometimes will find himself or herself in the position of pharmacy manager just by the nature of the business. The pharmacist who has been at the store location the longest will sometimes automatically become the manager, which is different from setting a goal of becoming a pharmacy manager. So what to do first? You may need to understand what a manager is before you can become one. Good managers identify with the goals of the organization and integrate the goals into their everyday actions. A manager also can be a leader by motivating others to understand why the goals are important to the success of everyone in the organization.

My advice for student pharmacists and staff pharmacists who want to be purposeful in their advancement is to network. Meet and get to know as many professionals as possible in the positions you are aspiring to hold in the future. Discover how they got to that position and how they stay there. Surround yourself with those in the position you desire. Take on additional responsibilities and make it clear that you have a goal and want to learn new things.

Q: How did you prepare to be a pharmacy manager?

I prepared by being willing to do whatever needed to be done. That may have been cleaning the floors, going to a store in another town to help or work, or learning the new computer system. By making yourself knowledgeable, valuable, and visible, you make yourself promotable.

My first position as a pharmacy manager was right after my graduation. I was still learning the increased responsibility of the pharmacist position. Luckily, I did not know enough to be scared. I continued to learn and did not assume I knew it all.

One trick I've learned through the years is to never go into a new location and pretend I know everything there is to know about that store. The staff at any location are valuable to a manager's success. Take time to become familiar with the current process before making changes.

Q: What challenges did you have as a new pharmacy manager?

My biggest challenge was to maintain a professional relationship with my staff and honor the personal connection I naturally feel for those I spend much time with. Now this is easier, at this point in my career, but as a young professional, I struggled with it.

As a pharmacy manager, I maintained as much control over my location and professional experience as possible. I had a sense of pride when the store location thrived and when patients complimented us. I also serve as a preceptor for the University of Maryland School of Pharmacy and have the opportunity to demonstrate to new student pharmacists the tasks and skills needed for a pharmacy manager position.

Q: What role has networking played in developing your personal and professional skills?

My position as pharmacy manager would not have been possible without the network of pharmacists I had early in my career. My professional activities allow me to continue learning and to be around those making changes and leading our profession. My past and present leadership roles in the Maryland Pharmacists Association and Lambda Kappa Sigma help me continue to develop managerial and leadership skills and professional knowledge.

Q: How can staff pharmacists grow to take on a management role?

Mentors who have guided me during my career have been valuable to the position I hold today. Staff pharmacists do not need to hold back because they do not yet hold a management position. Find the opportunity to show that you have the skills and leadership qualities that make a good manager. Once in the position, continue to learn, lead, and be a mentor yourself to be the best manager and leader in pharmacy.

Exercise 1-1 | **Best Manager, Worst Manager**

Complete this chart to evaluate the characteristics of the best and worst managers or preceptors you've ever worked with—which helps you think about the kind of manager *you* want to be. Use a pencil so you can revisit this exercise later, as your viewpoints change.

The characteristics of the worst manager or preceptor I ever had (Include those characteristics you want to avoid)	The characteristics of the best manager/preceptor I ever had (Include those characteristics you would like to develop)

Characteristics (in priority order) that I need to work on developing:

1.

2.

3.

4.

5.

6.

What I learned from this exercise:

Exercise 1-2 | **Checklist for New Pharmacy Manager**

Use this checklist to identify areas of opportunity for drawing on skills you have used in previous positions and applying them to the role of pharmacy manager. New skills will take time to learn and practice, and you should prioritize the ones that need more concentration.

Skill or competency	Part of my previous position/ responsibilities	Part of my new pharmacy manager responsibilities	Priority level for development of new responsibilities (1=High, 2=Medium, 3=Low)
Adapting my style to meet others' needs if indicated			
Assessing performance			
Assigning job responsibilities			
Coaching			
Creating a vision; having a "big picture" perspective			
Delegating			
Fostering innovation or creativity			
Hiring			
Interviewing			
Leading a team			
Making presentations/hosting meetings			
Managing the level of workplace activity and stress			
Motivating others			
Providing direction			
Providing leadership			
Recruiting/hiring			
Setting goals			
Supervising employees			
Supporting developmental opportunities for team members			
Time management			

Exercise 1-3 | Adapting Your Managerial Style

Use this chart to think about how you may have to adapt your management style to complement the needs and developmental level of your pharmacy team members.

- Who needs more direction?

- Who needs more support?

- Who should you leave to complete their tasks/duties on their own as much as possible?

Use the following guidelines to focus on each employee in the pharmacy, his or her needs, and the management that could and should be used to help each person perform the best and feel motivated.

Developmental levels of employees

Beginning level: New to the job, perhaps new to the pharmacy. Needs directions, supervision, and support. May have low competence level because of inexperience. May be enthusiastic about his/her new opportunity.

Moderate level: Has developed competence, but is not currently performing at a peak level. Needs coaching and support. May become disillusioned as the reality of the position and the duties/challenges becomes apparent.

High level: At peak performance, most likely very experienced. Needs less direct supervision and in some cases may resent such supervision. Think about ways to delegate tasks and new initiatives to keep the person feeling challenged.

Direct Report	Developmental Commitment Level	Appropriate Managerial Style [refer to Table 1-3]
Example: Mark Jones, CPhT	High level: Mark has been a nationally certified technician at your pharmacy for over 10 years. He has expressed boredom with his daily technician tasks.	Supportive: talk with Mark and observe him in his role to determine his areas of strength and opportunity. Delegating: provide Mark with a specialized task or responsibility, such as the training of new pharmacy team members.

continued on page 28

Exercise 1-3 | **Adapting Your Managerial Style,** *continued*

Direct Report	Developmental Commitment Level	Appropriate Managerial Style

Additional Resources

- *Becoming a Manager: Mastery of a New Identity.* Hill LA. Boston: Harvard Business School Press; 1992. This book examines the experiences of 19 first-year managers. It addresses adjusting to formal authority and setting agendas as well as accomplishing work through others and building alliances. How new managers can learn from their experiences is also covered.

- **The Manager's Job: Folklore and Fact.** Mintzberg H. *Harvard Business Review*; March/April 1990:163–76. This book provides an exploration of the interpersonal role, informational role, and decisional role of a manager by studying five CEOs and looking at other studies of managers.

- *The New Manager's Survival Manual.* Carr C. New York: John Wiley & Sons; 1995. This manual is a concise guide with tips for new managers entering their first year of management.

- **What It Really Means to Manage: Exercising Power and Influence.** Hill LA. Harvard Business School Case Note, February 15, 2000. Available at: http://acishost.acis.org.co/pipermail/geproyinfo/attachments/20090324/995df1f5/attachment-0001.pdf. This case study describes the realities versus the myths of what it means to be a manager and provides a framework for exercising influence and building networks of alliances for effective management.

- *The Wisdom of Teams: Creating the High-Performance Organization.* Katzenbach JR, Smith DK. New York: HarperCollins Publishers; 1999. This book provides information on the importance of teams—understanding teams and their purpose, how to form and become a team, and how to elevate the team to its high-performing potential.

References

1. Harvard Business School ManageMentor PLUS online program. *Becoming a Manager*. Boston: Harvard Business School Publishing; 2009.

2. Hirschhorn L. *Managing in the New Team Environment: Skills, Tools, and Methods*. Reading, Mass: Addison-Wesley Publishing Co; 1991:14–16.

3. McDonough RP, Bennett MS. Improving communication skills of pharmacy students through effective precepting. *Am J Pharm Educ*. 2006;70(3):58.

4. Berger BA. *Communication Skills for Pharmacists: Building Relationships, Improving Patient Care*. 3rd ed. Washington, DC: American Pharmacists Association; 2009: 15–20, 31.

Pharmacy Management and the Law

Federal Laws and Regulations

The United States has a number of employment laws that were developed to protect and advance the workforce. No matter what level of responsibility you have for recruitment and hiring, you should be familiar with these employment laws to ensure compliance with federal standards.

When reviewing and applying employment laws, pharmacy managers should remember that the laws are intended to help all Americans recognize and reap the benefits of diversity[1] and to help employers focus on the potential performance of individuals—and subsequently, their companies or institutions. Table 2-1 contains an overview of employment laws in the United States.

It's important for pharmacy managers to fully understand laws and regulations pertaining to pharmacy. This chapter gives you an overview of the following:

- Employment laws

- Federal regulations

- State and organizational considerations

Table 2-1 | **United States Federal Employment Laws**

Employment Law	Description of the Law	Covered Employees
Fair Labor Standards Act of 1938 (FLSA)	Establishes current minimum hourly wage and exemptions, overtime pay, recordkeeping, and child labor standards affecting full-time and part-time workers in the private sector and in federal, state, and local governments. This law requires overtime pay at 1½ times the regular rate of pay for all hours worked in excess of 40 hours per week. The federal minimum wage provisions are contained in the FLSA. Many states also have minimum wage laws, which can be found at www.dol.gov/whd/minwage/america.htm.	• All employees except those who qualify for narrow definitions of professional, executive, or administrative positions.
Equal Pay Act of 1963	Requires that men and women in the same workplace be given equal pay for equal work. The jobs do not have to be identical, but they must be substantially equal. Job content (not job titles) determines whether jobs are substantially equal. All forms of pay are covered by this law, including salary, overtime pay, bonuses, stock options, profit sharing and bonus plans, life insurance, vacation and holiday pay, cleaning or gasoline allowances, hotel accommodations, reimbursement for travel expenses, and benefits.	• Any employee who can prove wages for the same work differing by gender. Covers both males and females.

Table 2-1 | *continued*

Employment Law	Description of the Law	Covered Employees
Age Dis-crimination in Employment Act of 1967 (ADEA)	Protects individuals who are 40 years of age or older from employment discrimination based on age. The ADEA's protections apply to both employees and job applicants. Under the ADEA, it is unlawful to discriminate against a person because of his/her age with respect to any term, condition, or privilege of employment, including hiring, firing, promotion, layoff, compensation, benefits, job assignments, and training. A job notice or advertisement may specify an age limit only in the rare circumstances where age is shown to be a "bona fide occupational qualification" reasonably necessary to the normal operation of the business.	• Employees aged 40 and older. • Employers with 20 or more employees for 20 weeks during current or prior year must comply with this law.
Americans with Disabilities Act of 1990	Provides civil rights protections to individuals with disabilities that are like those provided to individuals on the basis of race, sex, national origin, and religion. It guarantees equal opportunity for indi-viduals with disabilities in employment, public accommodations, transportation, state and local government services, and telecommunications.	• Disabled individuals or individuals who are associated with a disabled individual (spouse or dependent). • Employers with 15 or more employees must comply with this law.

continued on page 34

Table 2-1 | **United States Federal Employment Laws,** *continued*

Employment Law	Description of the Law	Covered Employees
Civil Rights Act of 1964 (amended through 1991)	Makes it illegal to discriminate against someone on the basis of race, color, religion, national origin, or sex. The Pregnancy Discrimination Amendment to this act prohibits decisions based on pregnancy. The law also makes it illegal to retaliate against a person because the person complained about discrimination, filed a charge of discrimination, or participated in an employment discrimination investigation or lawsuit. Also requires that employers reasonably accommodate applicants' and employees' sincerely held religious practices, unless doing so would impose an undue hardship on the operation of the employer's business.	• Employers that control how work is done or if employees' work is essential to the business. • Employers with 15 or more employees for 20 weeks in current or prior year must comply with this law.
Family and Medical Leave Act of 1993	Provides an entitlement of up to 12 weeks of job-protected, unpaid leave during any 12-month period to eligible, covered employees for the following reasons: Birth and care of the eligible employee's child, or placement for adoption or foster care of a child with the employee. Care of an immediate family member (spouse, child, parent) who has a serious health condition. Care of the employee's own serious health condition. It also requires that employee's group health benefits be maintained during the leave.	• Workers employed for 25 hours per week or more for one year. • Employers with 50 or more employees within a 75-mile radius must comply with this law.

Table 2-1 | *continued*

Employment Law	Description of the Law	Covered Employees
Genetic Information Nondiscrimination Act of 2008	Makes it illegal to discriminate against employees or applicants because of genetic information. Genetic information includes information about the genetic tests of an individual and his or her family members, as well as information about any disease, disorder, or condition of an individual's family members (i.e., an individual's family medical history). Also makes it illegal to retaliate against a person because the person complained about discrimination, filed a charge of discrimination, or participated in an employment discrimination investigation or lawsuit.	Employers with 15 or more employees must comply with this law.

Sources: Adapted from the following:

The Fair Labor Standards Act of 1938, Pub Law 75-718, ch. 676, 52 Stat. 1060, June 25, 1938, 29 USC. Available at: http://www.dol.gov/compliance/laws/comp-flsa.htm. Accessed April 25, 2011.

Equal Pay Act of 1963, Pub Law 88-38, 77 Stat. 56, codified as amended at 29 USC § 206(d). Available at: http://www.eeoc.gov/laws/statutes/epa.cfm. Accessed April 25, 2011.

The Age Discrimination in Employment Act of 1967, Pub Law 90-202, Code, 29 USC. § 621 through 29 USC. § 634. Available at: http://www.eeoc.gov/laws/statutes/adea.cfm. Accessed April 25, 2011.

Titles I and V of the Americans with Disabilities Act of 1990, Pub Law 101-336, 104 Stat. 327, enacted July 26, 1990, codified at 42 USC § 12101. Available at: http://www.eeoc.gov/laws/statutes/ada.cfm. Accessed April 25, 2011.

Title VII of the Civil Rights Act of 1964, Pub Law 88-352, 78 Stat. 241, HR 7152. Available at: http://www.eeoc.gov/laws/statutes/titlevii.cfm. Accessed April 25, 2011.

Family and Medical Leave Act of 1993, Pub Law 103-3; 29 USC § 2601; 29 CFR 825. Available at: http://www.dol.gov/compliance/laws/comp-fmla.htm. Accessed April 25, 2011.

The Genetic Information Nondiscrimination Act of 2008, Pub Law 110-233, 122 Stat. 881. Available at: http://www.eeoc.gov/laws/statutes/gina.cfm. Accessed April 25, 2011.

> Employment laws are intended to help Americans benefit from diversity and to help employers focus on potential performance.

Sexual Harassment

Sexual harassment has been the focus of many court cases in recent years and is considered a form of employment discrimination. There are two types of sexual harassment:[2]

- **Quid Pro Quo Harassment** occurs when submission to unwanted sexual activity is explicitly or implicitly made a term or condition of the person's employment (i.e., "if you go on a date with me, I will consider you for a promotion"). This form of harassment is a result of an individual being approached.

- **Hostile Work Environment Harassment** occurs when unwelcome sexual conduct is severe or pervasive so that it alters the conditions of employment and creates an abusive work environment. This form of harassment is the result of an individual being approached or when an outside individual is a witness to such behavior.

All pharmacy practice settings must have a clear sexual harassment policy outlining complaint procedures and the processes that should be followed to address these complaints. In such cases, your behavior as a pharmacy manager can significantly influence the degree to which your employer can be held liable for your employees' actions. Pharmacy managers are required to protect employees from unlawful sexual and other discriminatory harassment from their supervisors, coworkers, vendors, and customers/patients. Most employers offer training and guidance on this important issue.

Omnibus Budget Reconciliation Act of 1990 (OBRA '90)

An important law to keep in mind regarding the proper management of patient medication usage and health outcomes is the Omnibus Budget Reconciliation Act of 1990 (OBRA '90). This federal law has several major components:[3]

- Prospective Drug Use Review

- Retrospective Drug Use Review

- Assessment of Drug Use Data

- Educational Outreach Program

Table 2-2 summarizes the pharmacy activities mandated by OBRA '90. After the law was enacted, each state had the opportunity to formulate its own state-specific regulations to respond to the OBRA '90 requirements. The states were required to address Medicaid recipients, and they could expand to other groups. Each state worked with its Medicaid officials and board of pharmacy to determine its own requirements. Table 2-3 gives a snapshot of the requirements that states put in place to respond to OBRA '90.

> **All pharmacy practice settings must have a clear sexual harassment policy.**

To ensure compliance with OBRA '90 and other pharmacy regulations, visit your state board of pharmacy website or state code of federal regulations. You can find contact information for each state board of pharmacy on the website of the National Association of Boards of Pharmacy (NABP) at www.nabp.net.

Table 2-2 | Overview of OBRA '90 Pharmacy Provisions

Prospective Drug Utilization Review (is the prescription necessary and appropriate?)
• Over or underutilization
• Therapeutic duplications
• Drug-disease interactions
• Drug-drug interactions
• Incorrect dosage or duration of treatment
• Drug-allergy interactions
• Clinical abuse and/or misuse

continued on page 38

Table 2-2 | **Overview of OBRA '90 Pharmacy Provisions,** *continued*

Patient Counseling Standards (an offer must be made to the patient to have a pharmacist counsel on prescribed medications)
  • Name of drug (brand name, generic, or other descriptive information)

  • Intended use and expected action

  • Route, dosage form, dosage, and administration schedule

  • Common side effects that may be encountered, including how to avoid them and the action required if they occur

  • Techniques for self-monitoring of drug therapy

  • Proper storage

  • Potential drug-drug or drug-food interaction or other therapeutic contraindications

  • Prescription refill information

  • Action to be taken in the event of a missed dose

Maintaining Accurate and Current Patient Profiles
  • Patient's full name

  • Address and telephone number

  • Date of birth or age

  • Gender

  • Drug profile

  • Pharmacist comments

  • Chronic conditions, allergies, and drug reactions

Source: Adapted from Vivian JC, Fink JL. OBRA '90 at Sweet Sixteen: A Retrospective Review. *US Pharm.* 2008; 33(3):59–65.

Table 2-3 | **States Enacting Various OBRA '90 Requirements**

Requirement	Number of States	Percentage of States
Medicaid patients only	5	10
All patients	45	90
New prescriptions only	32	64
New and renewal prescriptions	16	32
Face-to-face counseling required	45	90
Patient medication records mandated	46	92

Source: Adapted from Survey of Pharmacy Law. Sec. XXIII-Patient Counseling Requirements. Mount Prospect, Ill: National Association of Boards of Pharmacy. CD-ROM; 2007:75–6.

Health Insurance Portability and Accountability Act (HIPAA) of 1996

People working in health care today are generally aware of the Health Insurance Portability and Accountability Act (HIPAA) of 1996, and anyone who sees a health care practitioner or receives prescription medications has likely heard of it because patients must sign notices regarding privacy practices. HIPAA is the federal law that establishes standards for the privacy and security of health information, as well as standards for electronic data interchange of health information.[4] You can find a general overview here: https://www.cms.gov/HIPAAGenInfo.

HIPAA does the following:

- Provides rights and protections for participants and beneficiaries in group health plans.

- Provides protections for coverage under group health plans that limit exclusions for preexisting conditions.

- Prohibits discrimination against employees and dependents based on their health status.

- Allows a special opportunity to enroll in a new plan to individuals in certain circumstances.

> HIPAA protects all individually identifiable health information that is held or transmitted by a covered entity, whether electronic, paper, or oral.

The privacy and security rules for HIPAA apply only to covered entities, which in general include:

- A health care provider that conducts certain transactions in electronic form.

- A health care clearinghouse.

- A health plan.

Individuals, organizations, and agencies that meet the definition of a covered entity under HIPAA must comply with the rule's requirements to protect the privacy and security of health information and must provide individuals certain rights with respect to their health information.[4]

Definition of Terms Related to the Health Insurance Portability and Accountability Act (HIPAA)

- **Acknowledgment of notification:** HIPAA privacy standards require that a covered health care provider with a direct treatment relationship make a good faith effort to obtain an individual's written acknowledgment of having received the provider's Notice of Privacy Practices. The patient acknowledgments must be retained for at least six years.

- **Covered entity:** Under HIPAA, a covered entity is a health plan, health care clearinghouse, or health care provider who transmits any health information in electronic form in connection with a HIPAA transaction.

- **Department of Health and Human Services:** The federal government department that has overall responsibility for implementing HIPAA.

- **Health care provider:** Under HIPAA, this is a provider of services, a provider of medical or health services, and any other person or organization that furnishes, bills, or is paid for health care in the normal course of business.

- **Health information:** Information, whether oral or recorded in any form or medium, that is created or received by a health care provider, health plan, public health authority, employer, life insurer, school or university, or health care clearinghouse and that relates to the past, present, or future physical or mental health or condition of an individual, the provision of health care to an individual, or the past, present, or future payment for the provision of health care to an individual.

- **HIPAA incidental use and disclosure:** A provision under the HIPAA privacy standards that protects a pharmacy from liability for uses and disclosures of protected health information (PHI) incidental to proper use or disclosure of PHI. However, incidental uses and disclosures are only permissible if the pharmacy has:

  1. Applied reasonable safeguards to protect the confidentiality of PHI.

  2. Implemented the minimum necessary standard, where applicable.

  The incidental use and disclosure provision should apply if a pharmacist is overheard counseling a patient, but only if the pharmacist has applied reasonable safeguards to avoid being overheard.

continued

- **Privacy officer:** HIPAA requires that each covered entity appoint a chief privacy officer responsible for developing and implementing policies to comply with the privacy rules. There also must be a contact person or means in place for customers to ask questions about privacy issues and submit complaints.

- **Protected health information:** Any information about health status, provision of health care, or payment for health care that can be linked to a specific individual.

- **Statute:** A law established by an act of the legislature. Under the United States and state constitutions, statutes are considered the primary source of law.

Pharmacies and HIPAA

Pharmacies are classified as a covered entity as a health care provider because they transmit information in electronic form in connection with a transaction form that the Department of Health and Human Services has adopted as standard.[4]

HIPAA protects all individually identifiable health information that is held or transmitted by a covered entity, whether electronic, paper, or oral. This information is known as "protected health information" (PHI). PHI that is found in the pharmacy includes:

- A patient's prescription record

- A patient's prescriber history

- A prescription hard copy

PHI may be used and disclosed only for the permissible purposes of treatment, payment, and health care operations. A pharmacist who discusses a patient's drug therapy with a prescriber does not need to worry about disclosing more PHI than the prescriber needs to know, because the minimum necessary standard does not apply to uses or disclosures of PHI made in the following situations:

- When providing treatment to the patient.

- In communication with the patient.

- Pursuant to a patient authorization.

- When filling in mandatory or situational fields in an electronic transaction.

- To the Department of Health and Human Services when required to comply with or enforce another law.

HIPAA privacy standards require all health providers, including pharmacies, to provide individuals with an adequate notice of the uses and disclosures of PHI, including the patient's rights and the health provider's responsibilities.[5] Table 2-4 lists the rights of patients from their pharmacy under HIPAA. Patients must have access to a contact person, such as a privacy officer, to answer questions about privacy issues and to submit any complaints.

Table 2-4 | **Patient Pharmacy Rights Under HIPAA**

Obtain a copy of the health provider's *Notice of Privacy Practices*.
Obtain a copy of his/her pharmacy records.
Request a change to his/her pharmacy records.
Obtain an account of disclosures (nonroutine use only).
Request a restriction of use and disclosures of protected health information (PHI) in writing.
File a complaint regarding privacy infractions.
Authorize in writing that PHI be used or disclosed for purposes other than treatment, payment, or health care operations.

Source: Adapted from United States Department of Health & Human Services-Consumer Rights. Available at: http://www.hhs.gov/ocr/privacy/hipaa/understanding/consumers/index.html. Accessed April 25, 2011.

Training and Considerations

All pharmacy personnel should be trained regarding HIPAA and the pharmacy's privacy policies and procedures. Only personnel scheduled to work in the pharmacy should be allowed access to PHI. Everyone should take the necessary steps to ensure that PHI is protected at all times. For example, when pharmacy personnel leave messages on patients' voice mail saying that medications are ready to be picked up, the names of medications should not be left on the voice mail system.

Patients' PHI is found throughout the prescription processing and patient counseling process—on computer screens and on paper. Table 2-5 provides elements that should be considered regarding PHI.[5] There are significant penalties for the pharmacy and the people working in the pharmacy for failing to comply with HIPAA privacy standards.

Table 2-5 | Protected Health Information (PHI) Considerations in the Pharmacy

Pharmacy Aspect Regarding PHI	Description of the Issue	Potential Avenues to Ensure HIPAA Compliance
Viewing of patient PHI	No patient or unauthorized person should be able to view any patient's PHI during any course of the prescription filling process— which includes dropping off a prescription, waiting for a prescription, being counseled, or picking up a prescription.	Pharmacy terminals and waiting prescription bin areas should be positioned so that waiting patients are not able to view PHI. No one should be allowed to view any PHI in the pharmacy unless the person has been trained in HIPAA and is scheduled to work in the pharmacy.
Speaking with patients or caregivers about issues involving PHI	Medication counseling and other information regarding prescribed medications are some examples of the kinds of things that may be discussed between members of the pharmacy and the patient or caregiver.	When communicating PHI to a patient or caregiver, always verify that you are speaking with the patient or a person authorized to act on behalf of the patient. Verification can be obtained by a valid photo identification as well as asking for the patient's birthdate or address. • Use the consultation area for patient consultation and counseling. • When speaking to patients or their caregivers, keep voices low so others do not hear the conversation. • Make every effort to avoid incidental use and disclosure.

continued on page 44

Table 2-5 | Protected Health Information (PHI) Considerations in the Pharmacy, *continued*

Faxing prescribers with PHI	Sending faxes to prescribers for refill authorizations, prior authorizations, and other patient prescription issues.	Always confirm fax numbers before faxing.
Request for a copy of a patient record by the patient	Patients often request copies for their own records, tax purposes, and pre-scription reconciliation by their physicians.	The patient should sign a form requesting this information. Ensure that the patient shows a photo identification before you provide the patient record.
Request for a copy of a patient record by a spouse, care-giver, or parent of the patient	Patient records may be requested for the patient's records as well as for legal or medical matters.	The patient record should be sent to the patient via U.S. mail to the address on record for the patient. The envelope must be marked "personal & confidential."
Request for a copy of a patient record by a personal representative (an individual who has legal authority to act on behalf of the patient)	Personal representatives may request a patient record for legal or medi-cal matters.	The request for patient record should be reviewed and approved by the HIPAA or privacy officer of the pharmacy. If a parent is picking up patient records for their minor children, each child profile should be signed by the parent.
Legal/regulatory request	Records may be requested for patient history, prescriber history, or prescription hard copy.	These types of requests require accounting under the HIPAA privacy standards. Obtain authori-zation from the HIPAA or privacy officer of the pharmacy before providing any information.
Return of prescription medication containing PHI	Prescriptions that have not been picked up may be returned to the pharmacy inventory or prescriptions may be returned by patients.	Medications being returned to the pharmacy inventory should have all PHI covered or use a black marker to block out the PHI on the label (de-identify the patient) so that no PHI can be read. Medications being returned by a patient must be classified as non-salable credit. The medication should be transferred to a new vial without patient labeling or use a black marker to block out the PHI on the label (to de-identify the patient information).

Table 2-5 | *continued*

Pharmacy trash	Pharmacy trash may contain information such as a patient's date of birth, sensitive personal information, prescription number, or medication name.	A confidential trash disposal program should be established for the pharmacy, and all PHI should be shredded.

Source: Adapted from United States Department of Health & Human Services-Consumer Rights. Available at: http://www.hhs.gov/ocr/privacy/hipaa/understanding/consumers/index.html. Accessed April 25, 2011.

The Combat Methamphetamine Epidemic Act of 2005

The Combat Methamphetamine Epidemic Act of 2005 established federal requirements for the sale of scheduled chemical products containing ephedrine, pseudoephedrine, and phenylpropanolamine.[6] These ingredients have been used in the illicit manufacturing of methamphetamine and amphetamine. Since the implementation of this law in 2006, the number of methamphetamine labs in the United States has dropped significantly.[6]

All states have to comply with the requirements of selling these over-the-counter (OTC) drug products, which include:

- Limiting the amount that can be sold per customer in a 30-day period.

- Restricting where the products can be placed. Consumers cannot have direct access to products containing these ingredients.

- Maintaining a written or electronic logbook of all of the products that are sold containing ephedrine, pseudoephedrine, and phenylpropanolamine. Consumers must show photo identification issued by the state or federal government.

- Training employees who are allowed to sell these products to consumers. For example, they must be instructed to verify that the name on the consumer photo identification matches the name the customer wrote in the logbook.

Some states have extended this law to make these OTC products available only by prescription, and there is discussion at the federal level of making these products prescription-only across the United States.

Haight Act of 2008

The Internet has become an important force in all sectors of health care, including pharmacy. The Haight Act was enacted into law in late 2008[7] to regulate online pharmacies in an effort to control "rogue" Internet pharmacies. The Haight Act was named for Ryan Haight, who died in 2001 at 18 years of age from an overdose of pain medication containing hydrocodone, a prescription that he ordered over the Internet.[8]

The Haight Act amends the Controlled Substances Act[9] by adding the statement that no controlled substance "may be delivered, distributed, or dispensed by means of the Internet without a valid prescription." It also specifies that a patient–practitioner relationship must exist for a prescription to be valid, which is consistent with various other provisions in federal and state law. The Haight Act stipulates that a valid patient–practitioner relationship must include at least one medical evaluation of the patient carried out in person. The Haight Act also enhances penalties for unlawfully dispensing controlled substances in Schedules III through V.

As a pharmacy manager, it is important to keep abreast of the latest mechanisms of service delivery, including those available via the Internet. Patients often have questions regarding the sources of their pharmacy services. Internet pharmacies now have certification and accreditation designations, such as the Verified Internet Pharmacy Practice Sites (VIPPS).[10] VIPPS is a designation seal issued by NABP to Internet pharmacy practice sites that have met NABP standards for Internet pharmacy compliance. As more regulations are developed to govern specific areas of Internet pharmacy services, the importance of certifying and accrediting Internet pharmacies will likely increase.

Electronic Prescribing of Controlled Substances

In March 2010, the Drug Enforcement Administration (DEA) issued an interim final rule covering electronic prescribing of controlled substances, which went into effect June 1, 2010.[11] This rule provides prescribers with the option of electronically prescribing controlled drugs. It also outlines procedures for pharmacies to receive, dispense, and store these prescriptions.

Before any pharmacy computer system can be used for electronic prescribing of controlled substances, it must be audited or certified by a third party and found to be in compliance with DEA requirements for recording, signing, storing, and transmitting information. As of this writing, no third parties had been approved to perform such certification. In addition, major processes and system changes must be in place before prescriber and pharmacy applications can be used for electronic prescribing of controlled substances. These include:

- Requiring two-factor authentication at signing, such as a password and either use of a token or fingerprint verification.

- Developing signature and record-keeping protocols.

- Enhancing reporting and auditing functionality.

- "Identity proofing," whereby providers must be authorized by a federally approved credentialing body to electronically prescribe controlled substances.

- Developing policies and procedures to address data entry, access control, and other aspects of the interim final rule requirements.

Currently, most prescribers and pharmacies in the United States are not positioned to meet the intricate requirements of this interim final rule. Pharmacy managers should begin reviewing their current and planned systems and software applications in anticipation of this rule being fully implemented.

Loss of Controlled Dangerous Substances (CDS)

Maintaining an inventory system that allows all medications in the pharmacy to be tracked is an important facet of pharmacy management. In this regard, each pharmacy must have methods in place to maintain an accurate count of controlled dangerous substances (CDS) in order to prevent CDS losses. Some techniques that have proven useful include:

- Double counting all CDS medications when dispensing.

- Generating a weekly, biweekly, or monthly inventory usage report of CDS medications and comparing it to the actual number of CDS medications in stock.

If a CDS loss occurs, regardless of how—whether theft or miscount—it should be reported in writing to the local DEA field office within one business day of discovery. Procedures that should be followed as soon as the circumstances of the CDS loss are clarified appear below.

- Report the loss on the DEA Form 106 (Report of Theft or Loss of Controlled Substances):[12] You can find this form online through the DEA's Office of Diversion Control at www.deadiversion.usdoj. gov/21cfr_reports/theft/index.html.

- Fax DEA Form 106 to the following entities:

  ○ DEA Field Division Office.

  ○ The State Board of Pharmacy.

  ○ Any personnel who should receive a copy within the organization, such as the pharmacy supervisor or operations manager, pharmacy owner, loss prevention, pharmacy operations, and legal department.

Using the link in the first solid bullet above, you can also complete the DEA Form 106 online and it will be sent electronically to the DEA field division office.

State Boards of Pharmacy

Each state has its own state board of pharmacy that oversees the pharmacy regulations and statutes that govern pharmacy practice. The board's purpose is to promote, preserve, and protect the health, safety, and welfare of the citizens of the state.

Overall Board Responsibilities

As a pharmacy manager, you must keep in mind that the board of pharmacy protects the public, not the profession of pharmacy.[13] The national organization that brings all individual state boards of pharmacy together is the

National Association of Boards of Pharmacy (NABP—found at www.nabp. net). NABP oversees the administration of the standardized examination that states use to evaluate applicants' competency for pharmacist licensure.

Boards of pharmacy are responsible for any aspect of the practice of pharmacy in their state, which may include:

- Licensing pharmacists.

- Licensing or registering pharmacy technicians, international pharmacists, and student pharmacists.

- Licensing pharmacies.

- Licensing wholesalers who ship drugs and devices into their state.

- Investigating and responding to any complaint brought to its attention about any entity that they license or register.

- Interpreting the state pharmacy act.

- Developing regulations pertaining to federal or state pharmacy statutes.

Pharmacy Technicians

Over the past several decades, pharmacy technicians have become the paraprofessional of the pharmacist. Pharmacy technicians work under the direct supervision of a licensed pharmacist and perform many pharmacy-related functions, which may include (as mandated by the state board of pharmacy):

- Processing and preparing medication and other health care products for patients.

- Working with third-party plans in the adjudication of patient insurance.

- Managing pharmacy inventory.

- Compounding medications.

- Scheduling pharmacy personnel (such as technicians and pharmacy clerks).

- Managing and maintaining aspects of the pharmacy that do not require oversight by a licensed pharmacist.

Pharmacy technicians can be trained in many different ways, including online technician training programs, classroom training programs, and on-the-job training programs. Most pharmacies have their own technician training programs, and programs are also available at trade institutions or community colleges. Some state boards of pharmacy provide a listing of programs, especially if the board must approve the program for technician registration and licensing purposes.

Two national certification examinations are available in the United States for pharmacy technicians:

- ExCPT Examination
  - Accredited by the National Commission for Certifying Agencies and administered by the National Healthcareer Association
  - Information available at www.nhanow.com/pharmacy-technician.aspx.
- Pharmacy Technician Certification Examination:
  - Accredited by the National Commission for Certifying Agencies and administered by the Pharmacy Technician Certification Board (PTCB).
  - Information available at www.ptcb.org.
  - PTCB is governed by the American Pharmacists Association (APhA), the American Society of Health-System Pharmacists (ASHP), the Illinois Council of Health-System Pharmacists, the Michigan Pharmacists Association, and the NABP.

By successfully completing either of these examinations the pharmacy technician earns the credential "CPhT," which corresponds to the professional title of certified pharmacy technician.

License Renewal

As a pharmacy manager, you need to be on top of the state board of pharmacy requirements and license renewals for a pharmacist and, if applicable, for a pharmacist-in-charge (PIC), as well as registration and license requirements and renewals for pharmacy technicians—all of which differ by state.

For example, some state boards do not designate the role of a PIC or pharmacy manager, yet may define the role of the licensed pharmacist in supervising delegated pharmacy acts. Other state boards of pharmacy *do* define PIC requirements, such as being responsible for the legal operation of the pharmacy and performing a controlled substances inventory when the PIC leaves a pharmacy's employment.

A listing of board of pharmacy websites to find information on the definition and responsibilities of the pharmacist and pharmacy technician can be found at www.nabp.net.

Quality Assurance

Unfortunately, prescription errors and other mistakes sometimes happen in a pharmacy. For this reason, it's important to have a mechanism in place for recording and capturing all dispensing incidents in pharmacy practice sites where medications and health care products are dispensed. A dispensing incident is defined as the incorrect dispensing of a prescribed medication. Dispensing incidents include:

- Incorrect drug: Medication dispensed is different from the medication prescribed.

- Incorrect strength: Strength of medication dispensed is different from that of the medication prescribed.

- Incorrect directions: Directions for use on the label are different from what was prescribed.

- Incorrect patient name on prescription label: Incorrect name on label or filled under an incorrect patient profile.

- Dispensed prescription to incorrect patient: Prescription dispensed is given to an incorrect patient at the time that the prescription is picked up or administered.

- Dispensing expired medication.

- Drug utilization review: Inappropriate override of allergy alert or drug interaction.

Tracking and Reporting

Errors can be tracked via paper or electronic means and can be handled strictly internally or reported to an external patient safety organization such as the Institute for Safe Medication Practices Medication Errors Reporting Program, found at www.ismp.org/orderforms/reporterrortoismp. asp. In any case, the purpose of reporting should be to gather information that helps get to the error's root cause. By determining the cause, better procedures can be formulated or retraining can be carried out so the error does not recur. Reporting shouldn't be used to place blame on individuals, but rather to learn from mistakes and share best practices that help avoid similar errors.

You can institute a wide range of quality assurance practices to reduce the occurrence of medication errors, as suggested in Table 2-6, which groups activities according to workflow area to ensure the accuracy of all dispensed prescriptions.

Table 2-6 | **Pharmacy Workflow and Quality Assurance**

Workflow Area	Quality Assurance Considerations
Drop-off and data entry	• Verify patient name, address, date of birth, and allergies. • Contact prescriber if further clarification is necessary when analyzing the drug name, strength, quantity, directions, or any aspect of the prescription. • Be aware of any High Risk Medication Alerts from the Institute for Safe Medication Practices (www.ismp.org) when selecting the medication. • If a verbal prescription order is received via telephone, either read back the information to the person giving the prescription or listen to the voice mail message at least two times.

Table 2-6 | *continued*

Preparation of the medication	• Keep the pharmacy workbench and work area free of clutter.
	• Keep the number of prescription labels and orders printed out for processing to a minimum.
	• Verify the National Drug Code of the manufacturer stock product against that printed on the prescription label or in the computer.
Pharmacist verification check	• Verify all aspects of the finished prescription or order (review hard copy of the prescription or order, visually inspect the product selected).
	• Conduct a prospective drug utilization review as specified by state legislation and/or regulation.
If applicable, prescription pickup by the patient	• Ask the customer to state the patient's full name and address.
	• Make an offer to counsel in accordance with state OBRA regulations.

Discovering an Incident

Even when solid quality assurance steps are in place, medication errors may still happen. If you discover a potential dispensing incident, do the following:

- Reassure the patient or his or her representative or caregiver that the incident will be investigated immediately.

  ○ Verify the patient's name, date of birth, and address.

  ○ Determine the patient's concern.

  ○ Verify data entry, pull hard copy of the prescription or order, and review the label.

  ○ Identify the product dispensed (dosage form, color, shape, markings, odor, consistency).

- ○ Determine if ingestion occurred. If so, determine the length of ingestion.

- ○ Determine if the patient experienced any adverse effect or reaction.

- Research and investigate the alleged incident promptly and professionally to verify that a dispensing incident has occurred.

- Contact the prescriber immediately if the patient has ingested the medication or therapy has been interrupted.

- ○ Inform the patient or his or her representative or caregiver that the prescriber has been notified and convey any specific prescriber directions.

- Apologize for the incident, regardless of who was responsible for it.

- Take all reasonable and necessary steps to remedy any problem for the patient.

- Correct the prescription immediately; ensure that the appropriate prescription is dispensed.

- Provide the corrected prescription at no or minimal charge to the patient.

- Offer and provide a refund for the prescription associated with the incident.

- If applicable, ask the patient to return the prescription associated with the incident.

- ○ If the patient refuses to return the prescription, the pharmacist's course should still be to correct the incident and provide the correct prescription.

- Report the incident to a pharmacy mid-level manager, owner, or other designated person, if applicable.

- Document the incident using the pharmacy's dispensing incident reporting mechanisms.

Professional Pharmacy Organizations

Just as pharmacists have a variety of practice settings to choose from, they can join many professional pharmacy organizations. These organizations have specific missions for their members and often work with national and state agencies in developing and implementing new regulations and initiatives for the pharmacy profession. They also provide training, resources, and information that pharmacists can use to develop their professional practice and acumen. Table 2-7 lists some of the professional organizations related to pharmacy.

It is highly recommended that pharmacy managers become involved in their local and state pharmacy associations—which serve many important functions, including helping you to stay abreast of the evolving national and state legislation regarding pharmacy and health care. As this chapter suggests, every day pharmacy managers must consider a wide range of regulatory issues. If you, and all pharmacists, take an active role in building and reshaping pharmacy and health care laws and regulations, you help improve the lives of the patients you serve every day.

Table 2-7 | Professional Pharmacy Associations

Pharmacy Association	Description	Website
Academy of Managed Care Pharmacy (AMCP)	Represents pharmacists and associates who serve patients and the public by applying managed care principles.	www.amcp.org
American Association of Colleges of Pharmacy (AACP)	Represents the interests of pharmaceutical education and educators.	www.aacp.org
American Association of Pharmaceutical Scientists (AAPS)	Represents pharmaceutical scientists internationally.	www.aaps.org
American Association of Pharmacy Technicians (AAPT)	Represents pharmacy technicians practicing in a variety of health care settings.	www.pharmacytechnician.com
American College of Apothecaries (ACA)	Dedicated to advancing professional pharmacy practice and serving the pharmacy profession.	www.americancollegeofapothecaries.com

continued on page 56

Table 2-7 | **Professional Pharmacy Associations,** *continued*

American College of Clinical Pharmacy (ACCP)	Provides leadership, education, advocacy, and resources for clinical pharmacists.	www.accp.com
American Pharmacists Association (APhA)	The first established professional pharmacy organization; considered the national professional society of pharmacists. Each state has an affiliate association.	www.pharmacist.com
American Society of Consultant Pharmacists (ASCP)	International professional association to advance the practice of senior care pharmacy. Some states have an affiliate association.	www.ascp.org
American Society of Health-System Pharmacists (ASHP)	Represents pharmacists in health-care systems. Some states have an affiliate association.	www.ashp.org
Board of Pharmacy Specialties (BPS)	Mission is to improve public health by recognizing and promoting specialized training, knowledge, and skills of pharmacist specialists.	www.bpsweb.org
International Academy of Compounding Pharmacists (IACP)	International professional association representing pharmacists and technicians who focus on pharmacy compounding	www.iacprx.org
National Association of Chain Drug Stores (NACDS)	Represents chain community pharmacy. Some states have an affiliate association.	www.nacds.org
National Community Pharmacists Association (NCPA)	Represents the nation's community pharmacies, including independent pharmacy owners. Some states have an affiliate association.	www.ncpanet.org

Matthew Shimoda, PharmD
Pharmacy Manager and Immunization Coordinator
SuperFresh Pharmacies

Q: What is your professional pharmacy background?

I have been in my current position since the beginning of
2009. From 1986 until 1998 I was the owner of HealthCare
Professionals, which consisted of four retail pharmacies, a long-term care
pharmacy, an infusion division with an outpatient infusion center, and a
medical equipment company. I was a member of field management for CVS/
pharmacy from 2001 until 2009, after parts of my company were acquired.

I have been involved in many pharmacy organizations over the years
including the Maryland Pharmacists Association (president, trustee); currently I serve as treasurer. I am a member of the Executive Committee of
the University of Maryland School of Pharmacy Alumni Association as well
as a past president. I teach the Management of Healthcare Systems elective
course at the University of Maryland as an adjunct faculty member.

Q: Describe the path you took into pharmacy management.

After earning my PharmD from the University of Maryland School of
Pharmacy in 1984, I didn't wait long before stepping into the world of
management. Four of my fellow graduates from that class chose academia
and hospital affiliations, which was the usual path for graduates at that
time, but I chose community practice. I spent my first year and a half as
a community pharmacist helping to start clinical programs and services
while staffing the two pharmacies in our group. Fortunately, the owner
of the pharmacy was always looking to the future and saw the need for
groundbreaking services we could provide in the community. He became
my mentor, and as I threw out ideas we could initiate using our newly
installed computers that helped us fill prescriptions, he rarely hesitated to
let me try them—including cholesterol screenings, diabetes education, and
training patients on the "new" technology of glucose monitors, ambulatory
services for infusion patients, and so on.

I found out quickly that this new freedom to explore brought a fair amount
of responsibility with it. The other members of the organization looked
to me (still a rookie!) to lead the way in implementing and maintaining

the new services. These were exciting and challenging times for a new graduate. The owner was in his early sixties and had been contemplating retirement for a while. Two years after I graduated from pharmacy school, he offered to sell his pharmacies to me and another staff member who was 20 years my senior. So much for easing into management!

Q: What helped prepare you for management?

I learned a lot from my professors in school, but a few did something more than teach the curriculum—they encouraged me to go beyond and apply what they taught to everyday life. That really grabbed my attention. I was active in organizations during school and found that the closer I was to others in leadership the better I understood the process and ultimate outcomes. This was an important lesson for me to learn; as I became "part of the process" it became much easier to move forward.

It's easy for new graduates to become overwhelmed with day-to-day events such as starting your career, paying off loans, and family obligations. But if you want to advance your career, it's equally important to stay involved. Become a member of your state pharmacy organization, even if only to earn continuing education credits and network with others in the profession, and stay active with your alumni association. Become a preceptor for pharmacy students as soon as possible. Mentoring others helps you keep up to date, and students continually challenge your thought process.

Q: Do you have advice for aspiring pharmacy managers?

Stay active in your work environment, and learn the structure and hierarchy of your organization. A common mistake pharmacists make is not letting supervisors know of their desire to move up in the organization. I don't mean that when you first meet your immediate supervisor you say you want his or her job, but express your desire to learn as much as you can about the process of moving toward management.

Also, lead by example. It may sound cliché, but this worked for me. If something is important, I felt that I must be willing to get involved—whether that meant taking out the trash when others were busy or coming in early to get things ready so everyone could start right away. I wanted to show that I was not only the leader, but also an active member of the team.

Q: What challenges can new managers expect?

There will not always be someone around to get advice from, which can be scary. After all, your decisions affect not only you, but others around you. Dealing with failure was a challenge for me. As a pharmacy supervisor with CVS/pharmacy, I was constantly being measured against the standard of the company, as well as against my peer supervisors, for metrics related to finances, service, etc. Our districts were usually made up of 15 to 20 individual pharmacies. Many times my metrics were not where they should have been, and it was easy to blame the measurement process, but inevitably I found that it came down to me. Taking these failures and looking for ways to involve my team in finding ways to improve always eased the pain and focused my efforts on the positive. We all fail occasionally, but quickly moving to focus my team on correcting problems instead of dwelling on them allowed for many more successes over time.

I also had trouble with rejection. I've been passed over in my career, and those experiences taught me the most. It can be humbling; most important is how I handled it. Showing support for those who moved ahead has always come back to me many fold. Always look for ways to move the process forward; don't drag it down.

Q: What makes a good manager and a good leader?

The two have many more similarities than differences. A good manager needs to be efficient in making sure that processes are followed and the end result remains consistent. A manager can add a structured environment that is conducive to effective workflow. Contrast that with a good leader, who needs the same result but goes about it in a different manner. Leaders encourage open, effective communication—which can boost a group's abilities. A good example is the legendary basketball coach John Wooden. He was the master of a rigidly structured system, both in practice and during games, but through this system he also taught his athletes important life skills. Leaders can use effective communication to achieve much broader goals.

The ultimate benefit of my role as a manager and leader has been seeing others I have taught, mentored, and worked with go on to succeed themselves.

Lenna Israbian-Jamgochian, PharmD
Regional Pharmacy Manager
Safeway

Q: What is your professional background?

I have worked for the past seven years as a regional pharmacy manager for Safeway, supervising nearly 30 pharmacies in Maryland and Virginia. I was a pharmacy manager for a little more than two years before being promoted to regional pharmacy manager. Previously I worked as a pharmacy manager for Safeway and as assistant pharmacy manager for Kroger.

I received my Bachelor of Pharmacy from The Ohio State University College of Pharmacy and my PharmD from Virginia Commonwealth University School of Pharmacy. My undergraduate degree is Bachelor in Biology from University of La Verne. I have certificates in immunization, diabetes education, and osteoporosis.

I serve on the Maryland Board of Pharmacy and was recently elected treasurer. I also chair the Compliance/Disciplinary Committee and serve on the Practice and Legislative Committees. I'm a member of the National Association of Boards of Pharmacy, American Pharmacists Association, Maryland Pharmacists Association, and Maryland Association of Chain Drug Stores, and I'm on the board of the Armenian American Health Association of Greater Washington.

Q: What advice would you give a student or staff pharmacist who has the goal of being a pharmacy manager?

The first step is to excel as a pharmacist. That starts and ends with patient care, from counseling your patients to ensure optimal outcomes to further strengthening your relationship with them. Ensure that you serve as their pharmacy home, knowing all of their medications, OTCs, dietary supplements, allergies, etc., and that you're the go-to person for any questions related to their medication regimes.

Go beyond dispensing to make pharmacy care a priority, including administering immunizations and conducting medication therapy management—activities that are important for the health of your patient and that also strengthen customer loyalty and your community pharmacy business model.

Pay attention to detail. Managers are responsible for regularly completing multiple reports to ensure compliance with state and federal laws and to protect patient health. As a result, look for every opportunity to learn from your pharmacy manager, volunteering to help complete reports and cover his or her responsibilities while he or she is on vacation. Taking initiative will not only increase your chances for promotion, but also ensure that you start on the right foot when you begin as a pharmacy manager.

Q: What prepared you to take a pharmacy manager position?

My patients have always been my top priority. As a result, I helped to build one of the busiest pharmacies in the state, with incredible customer loyalty. I also worked closely with my pharmacy manager to learn how to complete all the required reports, conduct inventories, and stay under budget. Finally, I served as a preceptor for pharmacy students, which helped to improve my management and training skills.

Q: What challenges did you have as a new pharmacy manager?

My key challenge was related to joining a new company with different systems. I had to learn a new computer system for labeling and patient profiles and new reports for tracking different criteria. It took a lot of additional work, but was essential to my success. In the meantime, I continued to excel as a pharmacist, nearly doubling the number of patients we served during my short tenure before being promoted to regional pharmacy manager.

Q: What benefits and rewards did you experience as a new pharmacy manager?

I took great personal satisfaction in having an impact on my patients, my community, and my staff. A great sense of accomplishment comes with being the one ultimately responsible for ensuring the overall success of your pharmacy. The pharmacy manager position put me in regular contact with upper management, which helped elevate my profile and resulted in a fairly quick promotion to regional pharmacy manager.

Q: How have networking, having a mentor, and being involved in professional associations helped you develop as a pharmacy manager?

Because our profession keeps evolving and is highly impacted by technology, networking is essential to meeting your full potential—both through the training and professional development that professional associations offer and through social opportunities where you interact with colleagues.

Q: What do you consider to be the attributes of a manager and leader?

I believe it is essential to lead by example, including:

- Prioritize patient care, especially if you want your staff to do the same.

- Pay close attention to detail in dispensing, reporting, auditing, budgeting, compliance, and virtually every aspect of the pharmacy business.

- Keep up to date on new medications and regulations to ensure optimal care for your patients and compliance with all applicable laws.

- Invest in your staff to build their competence and their commitment to ensuring the success of the pharmacy.

- Get involved, both to stay current and to advocate for changes that will improve your patients' health and their access to your services.

Exercise 2-1 | My State Mandates for Pharmacy

Complete this chart to describe the mandates and requirements of the state where you are working as a pharmacist.	
State of Pharmacy Licensure:	
State Board of Pharmacy Website:	
Pharmacy Regulation/Issue	**Requirement(s) Mandated by the State**
Pharmacist Issues	
Pharmacist-in-Charge (if defined) Issues	
Pharmacy Technician Issues	
OBRA '90	
HIPAA Issues	
Sale of products containing ephedrine, pseudoephedrine, and phenylpropanolamine	
DEA Field Division Office	
Electronic prescribing of controlled substances	

Exercise 2-2 | My Employer's Requirements

Complete this chart to describe your employer's processes and requirements for HIPAA, quality assurance, and other regulatory issues.	
Pharmacy Issue	**Requirement(s) Mandated by My Employer**
Request for a copy of a patient record by the patient	
Request for a copy of a patient record by a spouse, caregiver, or parent of the patient	
Request for a copy of a patient record by a personal representative (an individual who has legal authority to act on behalf of the patient)	
Legal/regulatory request	
Return of prescription medication containing PHI	
Pharmacy trash	
Loss of controlled dangerous substances	
Medication incidents	

Additional Resources

- *Complete Guide to Human Resources and the Law.* Schilling D. New York: Aspen Publishers; 2005. This guide contains practice information on human resource laws and best practices for all work sites.

- **Department of Labor:** www.dol.gov Here you find the latest information from the United States Department of Labor, including labor laws, statistics, and resources.

- **Employment Law Information Network:** www.elinfonet.com This website provides information on employment law, including state laws and associated issues.

- **Labor Law for Supervisors.** Zachary MK. *Supervision.* 2000;61(4):23–6. This article covers labor laws that supervisors should be aware of for optimal compliance in the work setting.

- **National Association of Boards of Pharmacy:** www.nabp.net This organization supports all the state boards of pharmacy in the United States. Its website provides the contact information for all of the state boards of pharmacy.

- *Pharmacy Practice and the Law.* 5th ed. Abood RR. Sudbury, Mass: Jones and Bartlett; 2008. This reference provides information on federal laws and how they pertain to pharmacy practice.

- **Social Security Administration:** www.socialsecurity.gov This is the official website of the United States Social Security Administration, which provides resources for businesses and employers.

- **United States Equal Employment Opportunity Commission:** www.eeoc.gov This is the official website of the United States Equal Employment Opportunity Commission, which is responsible for enforcing federal laws pertaining to employment.

References

1. Wick J. Supervision of pharmacy personnel. *J Am Pharm Assoc.* 1998;38(4):457–68.

2. Gotkin V, Ross LA. Employment law essentials. In: Chisholm-Burns MA, Vaillancourt AM, Shepherd M, eds. *Pharmacy Management, Leadership, Marketing, and Finance.* Sudbury, Mass: Jones and Bartlett; 2010:335–49.

3. Vivian JC, Fink JL. OBRA '90 at sweet sixteen: A retrospective review. *US Pharm.* 2008;33(3):59–65.

4. Families USA: Portability in Health Coverage (HIPAA). Available at: http://www.familiesusa.org/issues/private-insurance/legal-rights/hipaa-and-portability-of.html. Accessed April 25, 2011.

5. U.S. Department of Health and Human Services. Health Information Privacy. Available at: http://www.hhs.gov/ocr/privacy/hipaa/understanding/consumers/index.html. Accessed April 25, 2011.

6. Combat Methamphetamine Epidemic Act of 2005 (Title VII of Public Law 109-177). Office of Diversion Control, Drug Enforcement Administration. Available at: http://www.deadiversion.usdoj.gov/meth/cma2005.htm. Accessed April 25, 2011.

7. Ryan Haight Online Pharmacy Consumer Protection Act of 2008. Available at: http://www.justice.gov/olp/pdf/hr-6353-enrolled-bill.pdf. Accessed April 25, 2011.

8. McKenna C. Ryan Haight Act will require tighter restrictions on internet pharmacies. *Government Technol,* October 2, 2008. Available at: http://www.govtech.com/gt/419355. Accessed April 25, 2011.

9. Comprehensive Drug Abuse Prevention and Control Act of 1970, Pub Law 91–513, 84 Stat. 1236 (1970), codified at 21 USC 801 et seq.

10. National Association of Boards of Pharmacy. Verified Internet Pharmacy Practice Sites. Available at: http://vipps.nabp.net/verify.asp. Accessed April 25, 2011.

11. Electronic Prescribing for Controlled Substances. Available at: http://www.deadiversion.usdoj.gov/ecomm/e_rx/index.html. Accessed April 25, 2011.

12. U.S. Department of Justice, Drug Enforcement Administration: Report of Theft or Loss of Controlled Substances. Available at: http://www.oregon.gov/Pharmacy/pdf/106form.pdf. Accessed April 25, 2011.

13. State Regulation of Pharmacy Practice. In: Abood RR, *Pharmacy Practice and the Law.* 5th ed. Sudbury, Mass: Jones and Bartlett; 2008:307–27.

Personnel Roles, Processes, and Issues

Pharmacies Rely on Teams

Any pharmacy operation, large or small, relies on a team of people to run smoothly and get the work done. And, as the pharmacy manager, many or all of these people report to you. Figure 3-1 shows typical pharmacy positions that the pharmacy manager oversees.

Nonlicensed, Nonregistered Personnel

Pharmacy personnel who are not licensed or registered with the state board of pharmacy are typically not defined in a consistent way in pharmacy practice. They may be classified as support staff, pharmacy aides, pharmacy associates, pharmacy clerks, pharmacy students, pharmacy interns, or pharmacy drivers. The duties of nonlicensed/nonregistered personnel may include the following:

> Most responsibilities of pharmacy managers relate in some way to personnel management. This chapter looks at:
>
> • Staff roles and management considerations
>
> • Hiring process
>
> • Motivating, delegating, and coaching
>
> • Handling conflicts

Figure 3-1 | **Direct Reports of a Pharmacy Manager**

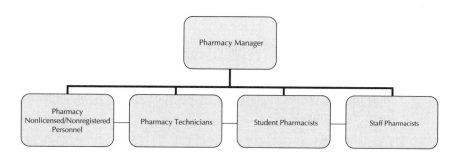

- Answering telephones and directing inquiries to the appropriate licensed/registered pharmacy staff.

- Assisting in inventory management.

- Carrying out clerical duties.

- Fielding questions from patients, customers, and other health care providers and routing them to the appropriate licensed/registered pharmacy staff.

- Greeting and assisting patients or customers.

- Maintaining patient confidentiality. (Regardless of their role, all workers should complete training about patient confidentiality, as discussed in Chapter 2.)

- Retrieving, counting, and measuring medications.

- Ringing up merchandise and prescriptions at a register.

- Stocking shelves.

- Carrying out other duties delegated to them that are appropriate for nonlicensed/registered personnel.

Pharmacy Technicians

Pharmacy technicians help licensed pharmacists prepare prescription medications and orders, provide customer service, and perform administrative duties. Over the past several decades, pharmacy technicians have become the pharmacist's paraprofessional. In other words, certain pharmacy tasks are delegated to them, but they are not licensed to practice as a pharmacist. Pharmacy technicians work under the direct supervision of a licensed pharmacist and perform many pharmacy-related functions, such as:

- Processing and preparing medications and health care products for patients.

- Working with third-party plans to adjudicate and reconcile patient insurance claims.

- Managing pharmacy inventory.

- Compounding medications.

- Handling pharmacy management duties that can be performed by nonlicensed personnel, such as scheduling pharmacy support staff.

Student Pharmacists
Student pharmacists work in pharmacy locations primarily to complete internships and externships.

Internships
An internship is a structured learning experience that is usually paid. The student pharmacist works in a pharmacy location, completing tasks and gaining skills. The internship may be for a limited time, such as during the summer only, or it may continue throughout the year. Most pharmacy locations have a series of tasks and competencies that constitute the predetermined goals of their pharmacy internships, such as those listed below. The tasks included and the depth of experience a student receives depend on the internship's length and purpose.

- Pharmacy technician functions

- Customer service

- Pharmacy operations

- Pharmacy business metrics

- Merchandising

- Leadership

- Delegation

- Effective communication

- Business management

Externships

Pharmacy externs are student pharmacists who are not paid when working in a pharmacy location. They are either working as part of their pharmacy school experiential requirement or are volunteering or "shadowing" a pharmacist to gain practical pharmacy experience hours for pharmacist licensure. The goal of experiential learning is to apply and synthesize knowledge and skills that pertain to patient-centered care and practice management.[1]

> Any pharmacy operation, large or small, relies on a team of people to run smoothly and get the work done.

The two types of experiential training for student pharmacists are described below. These are a required part of training to become a pharmacist, giving students the opportunity to apply didactic knowledge and gain hands-on experience.

- Introductory pharmacy practice experiences (IPPEs) are carried out in community and institutional practice settings, allowing students, under appropriate supervision and practice regulations, to assume direct patient care responsibilities.[2]

- Advanced pharmacy practice experiences (APPEs) expand on the skills students learn in IPPEs and can take place in a variety of pharmacy practice settings. APPEs include dispensing, counseling, and extensive patient care responsibilities related to proper medication use, such as monitoring for safety and efficacy and documenting the care provided.[2]

Each school of pharmacy provides its own requirements for IPPEs and APPEs. You can find a current listing of pharmacy schools in the United States on the website of the Accreditation Council for Pharmacy Education (ACPE) at http://www.acpe-accredit.org/shared_info/programsSecure.asp.

See Table 3-1 for a listing of activities that can be explored during IPPEs and APPEs.

Table 3-1 | Activities for Pharmacy Practice Experiences

Introductory Pharmacy Practice Experience (IPPE) Activities	Advanced Pharmacy Practice Experience (APPE) Activities
Shadowing practitioners or APPE students	Practicing as a member of an interprofessional team
Processing and dispensing new and refill medication orders	Identifying, evaluating, and communicating to the patient and other health care professionals the appropriateness of the patient's specific medication regimen
Conducting patient interviews to obtain patient information	Consulting with patients regarding self-care products
Responding to drug information inquiries	Recommending prescription and nonprescription medications, dietary supplements, diet, nutrition, and complementary and alternative therapies
Interacting and communicating with other health care practitioners	Identifying and reporting medication errors and adverse drug reactions
Interpreting and evaluating patient information	Providing patient and health care provider education
Billing third parties for pharmacy services	Accessing, evaluating, managing, and using clinical and scientific publications in the decision-making process
Presenting patient cases	Accessing, evaluating, and applying information to promote optimal health care
Documenting interventions in patient records	Conducting drug use review
Conducting physical assessments	Participating in the pharmacy's quality improvement program
Administering medications	Participating in purchasing and other pharmacy planning processes
Providing point-of-care and patient-centered services	Participating in the design, development, marketing, and reimbursement process for new patient services
Interpreting and evaluating patient information	Participating in discussions and assignments of human resources management, medication resources management, and pharmacy data management systems, including pharmacy workload and financial performance

Source: Adapted from *Accreditation Standards and Guidelines for the Professional Program in Pharmacy Leading to the Doctor of Pharmacy Degree,* adopted January 15, 2006. Available at: http://www.acpe-accredit.org/pdf/ACPE_Revised_PharmD_Standards_Adopted_Jan152006.pdf. Accessed April 25, 2011.

Staff Pharmacists

A staff pharmacist's responsibilities depend on the practice setting and organizational goals and will mirror the responsibilities of the pharmacy manager. Potential duties of a staff pharmacist may include:

- Overseeing the dispensing of medications according to prescriptions or orders issued by an authorized prescriber.

- Performing or overseeing packaging, labeling, measuring, compounding, storing, charging, and recording medications used in patient care.

- Reviewing prescriptions or orders to check appropriateness of therapy, determine ingredients needed, and ensure correct dosage.

- Ordering and maintaining the supply of drugs, chemicals, and other pharmaceutical stock items.

- Advising patients and care providers of potential drug interactions, possible side effects, storage information, and instructions on how to use medications.

- Presenting lectures to medical nursing staff, physicians, and other groups on medications and matters pertaining to pharmacy.

- Preparing sterile products for patient administration; determining proper preparation, packaging, sterilization, storage, and stability requirements of the product.

- Helping clinicians establish the proper protocols, storage, distribution, and administration procedures for investigational drugs.

- Training and supervising nonlicensed/nonregistered personnel and pharmacy technicians, as assigned.

- Developing or participating in clinical pharmaceutical research.

- Serving as a preceptor for student pharmacists.

The Human Resources Management Continuum

Human resources (HR) management has many facets; you can think of the process as a continuum, starting with bringing employees on board, then helping them grow and excel and dealing with issues that arise. The bullets below list key areas of HR, which are discussed in the following pages.

- The hiring process

- Employee motivation

- Delegation to employees

- Coaching and counseling

- Conflict resolution

The Hiring Process

Hiring employees is one of the most pivotal activities a pharmacy manager must perform to have a productive workplace. To be effective, the hiring process must involve eight key components,[3] which are listed in the box below.

Eight Steps in the Hiring Process

1. Evaluate current staffing needs.

2. Define position requirements.

3. Decide who will be involved in the hiring process.

4. Develop a sourcing strategy.

5. Design a screening and evaluation process.

6. Negotiate a competitive employment offer.

7. Provide a thorough and welcoming orientation.

8. Evaluate the effectiveness of the hiring process after a candidate is on the job.

Source: Adapted from Lee CD, Bradley-Baker LR. Successful recruitment and hiring strategies. In: Chisholm-Burns MA, Vaillancourt AM, Shepherd M, eds. *Pharmacy Management, Leadership, Marketing, and Finance.* Sudbury, Mass: Jones and Bartlett; 2010:187–214.

Step 1. Evaluate Current Staffing Needs

Determining the roles needed in the pharmacy calls for careful analysis. Putting thought and time into examining the pharmacy's staffing requirements will result in better hiring decisions.

During this step, you must explore and answer the following questions:

> Hiring employees is one of the most pivotal activities a pharmacy manager must perform to have a productive workplace.

- What work needs to be accomplished?

- What would be the outcomes if the position were not filled?

- What are the skills and abilities needed to do this work?

- Is there anyone currently working at the pharmacy or in the department or organization who can be trained to do this work?

- Is this a full-time or part-time position?

Step 2. Define Position Requirements

You need to create a position description that clearly outlines the duties, tasks, and responsibilities for the job. A well-defined job description is a key tool that you use not only when recruiting and selecting employees, but also for compensation decisions, training requirements, and performance evaluation. Be sure it includes essential functions—that is, those that are fundamental for doing this particular job. If a position description already exists from a previous hiring cycle, review it carefully and update it to match your current needs.

An excellent online resource to help you with job descriptions is O*Net, the Occupational Information Network, found at www.onetcenter.org. The O*Net database, produced by the U.S. Department of Labor, contains hundreds of occupation-specific descriptors and is continually updated.

Step 3. Decide Who Will Be Involved in the Hiring Process

When you're responsible for making a hiring decision, it's common to seek assistance from colleagues. A pharmacy manager might ask pharmacists and technicians who work at the pharmacy to help screen applications or interview job candidates.

Step 4. Develop a Sourcing Strategy

A sourcing strategy is the set of tactics an organization uses to find applicants for vacancies. The many sources you can use for finding candidates for pharmacy positions include:

- Advertising the position in professional journals, newsletters, newspapers, and online, including the company website and through job search engines such as CareerBuilder.com and Monster.com.

- Direct mailers sent as bulk advertisements as well as recruitment letters addressed directly to the pharmacist.

- Job and career fairs.

- Employee referrals.

- Internship and externship opportunities at the pharmacy location.

- Networking through pharmacy organizations, pharmacy schools, and professional networking.

- Search firms and "headhunters."

- Visiting competitors, also known as "cold-calling" or "store visitations."

Step 5. Design a Screening and Evaluation Process

Once you've launched your sourcing strategy, you'll probably get several applicants for the advertised position. It's important to have effective screening and evaluation approaches in place to help you choose among applicants, such as the following:

- Reviewing written or electronic application materials, such as the cover letter, résumé, credentials, transcripts, and application. In large companies, the HR department may screen résumés and pass on to the manager only those that meet certain criteria.

- Interviewing in person, by telephone, or via videoconference. Interviews should be structured to include a predefined set of questions and a standardized method of evaluating responses.

In large companies and chain organizations, the HR department may carry out initial telephone screening interviews and forward the information to the local or regional pharmacy manager.

- During the interview process, ask questions that relate only to the position's essential functions or to how the candidate might work within a given environment.

- Avoid asking inappropriate, unethical, or illegal questions,[4] such as those related to:

  - Age

  - Marital status

  - Ethnic origin

  - Religion

  - Mode of transportation to work

  - Arrest record

- Completing pre-employment screening before officially hiring and onboarding a candidate. In fact, employment offers are generally contingent upon the outcome of the following:

  - Reference checks

  - Background checks

  - Drug test

Step 6. Negotiate a Competitive Employment Offer

Once you select a final candidate, you must present a competitive employment offer package containing total compensation, including salary and other employer-paid benefits such as health insurance and paid time off. The offer should be in writing and should confirm the terms and conditions of employment using standard language required by the HR department or legal counsel. Figure 3-2 presents an example of a pharmacy technician employment job offer.

Figure 3-2 | Sample Pharmacy Technician Employment Offer

New Day Pharmacy   Date
2 Main Street
New Town, USA

Jane Doe
111 Anyplace Street
New Town, USA

Dear Ms. Doe:

It is my pleasure to extend the following offer of employment to you on behalf of New Day Pharmacy. This offer is contingent upon your passing our mandatory drug screen and a criminal background check. Instructions and the documents for taking the drug test within five days of acceptance of this offer are included with this offer. Instructions and the document for the criminal background check are also included with this offer and should be returned with your signed employment offer letter. A copy of your state pharmacy technician registration should also be returned with your signed employment offer letter.

Title: Pharmacy Technician

Reporting Relationship: The position will report to Jane Joe, RPh, Pharmacy Manager.

Job Description: The description is attached to the employment offer.

Base Salary: Will be paid in bi-weekly installments of $_____, which is equivalent to $_____ on an annual basis, and subject to deductions for taxes and other withholdings as required by law or the policies of the company.

Benefits: The current, standard company health, life, disability, and dental insurance coverage is supplied per company policy. Eligibility for other benefits, including the retirement program, will take place per company policy. Employee contribution to payment for benefit plans is determined annually.

Vacation and Personal Time Off: Vacation is accrued at X.XX hours per pay period, which is equivalent to two weeks on an annual basis. Personal days are accrued per company policy.

Start Date: {Insert Date}

Your employment with New Day Pharmacy is at-will and either party can terminate the relationship at any time with or without cause and with or without notice.

If you are in agreement with the terms of this offer, please sign below and return to my attention in the self-addressed stamped envelope. This offer is valid until {Insert Date}.

Please contact me at {Insert Pharmacy Telephone Number} with any additional questions or concerns.

Signatures:

_____
Mary Smith, RPh, Pharmacy Manager, New Day Pharmacy   Date

_____
Jane Doe   Date

Step 7. Provide a Thorough and Welcoming Orientation

An orientation is a program that helps a newly hired employee become familiar with the position and organization. A proper orientation sets the baseline for retention and success.

The orientation should include training to prepare the employee for his or her new role. The training should consist of the following:

- Mandatory elements related to law and policy, such as the Health Insurance Portability and Accountability Act (HIPAA).

- Hard-skill elements and knowledge necessary to perform the position, such as computer training.

- Soft-skill elements involving competency-based practical skills, such as time-management training.

A training program may also have an assessment component following the formal training, such as a written test, verbal evaluation, or demonstration of the position skills and responsibilities. You should reassess your training program at least once a year to ensure that it covers all items in the job description and reflects any changes in the position responsibilities that call for new information regarding laws, federal regulations, or board of pharmacy issues.

The orientation and training program are all part of what is known as "onboarding"; that is, acquiring, accommodating, and assimilating new employees in a new work environment. Onboarding can include setting up employee access to online systems as well as a mentoring program, social events, self-evaluations, and feedback sessions.

Step 8. Evaluate the Effectiveness of the Hiring Process

Validating the success of the hiring process boils down to determining that the candidate is a successful employee.[5] Fundamental to an employee's success is knowing the manager's expectations.

Job descriptions outline basic expectations about the employee's activities, performance, and time frame for certain tasks or achievements.[6] Effective coaching and counseling should precede any kind of formal or informal performance evaluation.

Providing employees timely and accurate feedback about their performance is essential to maintaining a productive work environment.[7] At least once a year, schedule a formal performance evaluation that you hold privately and in person, in which you review with the employee a written assessment you've developed of the employee's strengths, goals, and areas for growth. Base the evaluation on specific expectations and goals related to the employee's current position as well as on general competency areas.

> Putting thought and time into examining the pharmacy's staffing requirements will result in better hiring decisions.

Performance evaluations serve as a learning tool and a yardstick for assessing accomplishments. They are also an important source of documentation. When pharmacy managers document an employee's performance based on measurable, legally defensible criteria, they are best positioned to withstand legal issues based on their employment decisions, including those related to promoting and terminating an employee.[7]

Motivating Employees

Job performance is essentially the product of one's ability, or skill, and one's motivation, or will. Here's another way to express this concept:

Job performance = (ability/skill) x (motivation/will)

To boost people's skills, you can train them, but motivating them is not so straightforward. Many managers find their role as motivators to be extremely challenging. How do you determine what makes the people you supervise want to learn more, sharpen skills, and take on greater responsibility? It's commonly believed that a high salary is a primary motivator, and although that may be true for some employees, in most cases other factors are even more powerful, such as:[8]

1. Work that is interesting and challenging. Employees want assignments that require them to use a variety of skills and determine their own solutions. Training is one tool that helps increase people's interest in their work and lower resistance to change.

2. Praise and recognition from peers and supervisors. Any type of recognition makes employees feel valued and important, which can in turn lead to improved productivity.

3. Opportunity for growth. Opportunities for promotion are a great motivator, but other kinds of changes can be, as well, such as expanded responsibilities or being assigned a specific new task, such as inventory management.

4. A comfortable work environment. The physical space must be conducive to employees' productivity and they must see evidence of continuous improvements to the equipment and facilities they need to do their work.

5. Empowerment. Employees want an atmosphere in which they can take responsibility and exercise the authority to use their skills and abilities to the greatest extent possible.

When you are trying to boost employees' motivation, you must do the following:[9]

- Provide positive reinforcement about their performance, skills, and abilities.

- Treat everyone fairly.

- Attempt to address employees' needs in a timely manner.

- Set realistic workplace goals accompanied by deadlines, when appropriate.

- Base rewards on job performance.

- Restructure a position and delegate tasks or responsibilities when employees have potential to advance or have indicated the desire to do more.

Delegating

Delegating involves assigning a task or project to another person and getting his or her commitment to complete it.[10] Delegation is one of the most important skills used by successful managers and is often neglected by overworked managers.

When you delegate a task, you prepare your direct reports for more responsibility and show your trust and faith in them. At the same time, you transfer accountability for maintaining established standards to the other person. The other person learns and grows while you free up your time to launch new projects or take on other responsibilities.

Examples of tasks that a pharmacy manager can delegate include:

- Preparing for third-party audits

- Doing daily and weekly paperwork

- Purchasing and billing

- Managing inventory

- Scheduling support staff

Table 3-2 presents things you should consider when delegating tasks to employees.

 Table 3-2 | Things to Consider When Delegating

Step	Considerations and Actions
Decide on the task to delegate.	Do not delegate anything that is required to be done by a pharmacist or manager.
Choose the employee who will have responsibility for the delegated task.	Take into account the details of the task as well as the qualifications and work ethic of those being considered to handle it.

continued on page 82

Table 3-2 | **Things to Consider When Delegating,** *continued*

Explain the task, in detail, to the employee.	Include the following: • What the task is. • Why the task needs to be done. • Where the task should be completed. • The time frame or frequency for completing the task. • Methods that can be used to complete the task.
Provide the employee with the tools needed to complete the task.	Tools may include the following: • Information. • Training. • Other personnel. • Contact information for people who may be able to assist.
Understand the employee's limitations.	Provide the necessary information or the additional training the employee needs to build skills so he or she will be able to complete the task.
Let the employee do the delegated task.	Step back and give the employee the freedom to carry out the task. Tell the employee who is available (managers, peers, etc.) to answer questions or address concerns the employee may have regarding the task.
Encourage the employee to talk about issues, challenges, or successes with a task.	Have the employee come back to you with questions, concerns, or new insights regarding the task. If the employee does not offer this information, the manager should periodically ask the employee for feedback.
Give the employee credit and feedback.	Provide periodic feedback during the course of the delegated task. Feedback should be more frequent at the beginning and then can be addressed at bi-yearly or yearly performance evaluations.

Coaching and Counseling

A good manager is also a coach who guides employees toward their goals and contributes to their development.[11] Coaching involves exploring, facilitating, partnering, and advising to help direct reports and colleagues learn and advance. Situations that open up opportunities for coaching include times when:

- A new member of the pharmacy team needs direction.

- A direct report is ready for new responsibilities.

- A team member undergoing problems with performance would benefit from guidance.

- A worker needs positive feedback and recognition to boost morale or reinforce positive efforts.

Beyond Performance Improvement

In the workplace, counseling can be defined as a discussion between manager and employee about real or perceived performance or job-related behavior.[11] Many managers avoid counseling situations because they find them unpleasant. However, you can make these discussions more inviting if you look at them as an opportunity to help the employee improve and contribute more successfully to the pharmacy. Let the employee give his or her perception of the identified behavior; then work together to correct it.

Coaching and counseling employees is not always about improving performance. It's also a tool for setting new goals and reinforcing an employee's good performance. To be a good coach, you must build your understanding of your employees by:

- Observing without judgment

- Listening actively

- Asking questions

To help your direct reports grow, you need to:

- Advocate their opinions to upper management, such as when a new process is rolled out that has unanticipated effects.

- Provide and receive feedback.

- Build agreement between parties, such as between you and the employee or between two employees. In other words, be a negotiator or mediator for issues that need consensus.

Feedback

Employees value knowing what their responsibilities are and receiving clear, consistent feedback regarding their performance. When used properly, feedback is a communication tool that helps employees develop professionally and focuses on their behavior—not on who they are. A feedback session should be:[11]

- **Balanced.** Provide corrective comments, which focus on behaviors the employee should change and improve, and affirming comments about things that went well and should be repeated in the future.

- **Consistent.** Treat all employees the same way, especially those who exhibit the same or similar behavior as the behavior you are discussing.

- **Timely.** Give feedback as soon as possible after the incident takes place or you witness the behavior. Give positive feedback immediately and in public whenever possible; give feedback in private when it's aimed at improving performance. As the saying goes, "praise in public, criticize in private."

- **Accurate.** Keep track of performance discussions and observations related to behavior and performance to be sure your feedback is grounded and supported. A calendar or logbook can be used for this purpose.

- **Constructive.** During the discussion, focus on problem-solving with the employee; do not use the time to embarrass or humiliate.

Conflict Resolution

Conflict is the mental struggle that stems from incompatible or opposing needs, drives, wishes, external demands, or internal demands.[12] Conflicts arise in the workplace, just as they do in every other part of life. At work, conflict situations can be defined as work behaviors or interactions with the potential to lead to undesired outcomes.[13] Workplace conflicts tend to fall in the following categories:

When workplace conflicts arise, managers often have to intervene to resolve the situation.

- **Interdependence conflicts.** These occur when a person's job or success depends on someone else's cooperation, input, or productivity. For example, if an employee is often late for his scheduled shift, other employees are affected in a negative way.

- **Differences in work style.** When individuals approach the work in different ways, it may lead to clashes. For example, some employees may delay doing weekly tasks that are assigned to be done on a certain day.

- **Differences in background.** Variations in educational background, personal experiences, ethnic heritage, generations, and political preferences can cause conflicts to arise.

- **Differences in leadership style.** People are not all the same in how they provide direction, implement plans, and motivate people— nor does everyone have the same preference for how they like to be led. Some people favor a more authoritative approach, while others are participative ("let's work on this together") or delegative ("you take care of it while I do something else").

- **Differences in personality.** Sometimes employees rub each other the wrong way or inadvertently "push buttons" simply because of traits and preferences that do not fit together easily.

Table 3-3 presents conflict management strategies. The strategy you use depends on the conflict itself as well as the information available when you become aware of the situation. Managers must address conflicts as soon as possible—especially when the conflict is impeding an employee's development or interfering with the pharmacy's success.

Table 3-3 | **Strategies for Managing Conflict**

Strategy	Description	Outcome	Advantages	Disadvantages
Collaboration	High concern with the interests of all people involved.	Win/Win	Builds commitment. Reduces negative feelings.	Takes a lot of time and energy.
Compromise	High concern for the manager's interests and moderate concern for the interests of others.	Win some/ Lose some	Less time-consuming. Avoids power struggles.	Important values and long-term objectives may be lost.
Competition	High concern for the manager's interests and less concern for the interests of others.	Win/Lose	The manager gets what he or she wants.	Conflict may escalate. The "losers" of the conflict may retaliate.
Accommoda-tion	Low concern for the manager's interests and high concern for the interests of others.	Lose/Win	This can be viewed as a goodwill gesture.	The manager's ideas and concerns don't get attention. The manager may lose credibility and influence.
Avoidance	Low concern for all person(s) involved.	Lose/Lose	Avoids the potential of damage that may arise from confrontation.	Important decisions may be made by default.

Source: Adapted from *The Manager's Guide to Negotiation and Conflict Resolution. Harvard Management Communication Letter Collection.* Boston: Harvard Business School Publishing; 2000.

People have preferred work and communication styles—which can spark conflicts in and of itself. Pharmacy managers have to consider their own work style as well as the styles of their employees. Table 3-4 provides information about four work styles with descriptions of how people in these categories work, what they seek, and how to work with them.

Table 3-4 | **Typical Work Styles**

Style Type	Description	How They Work	What They Seek	How to Work with Them
Director	Task-oriented people who like to take charge of people and situations. They tend to be competitive.	They do things their way and will go to extremes to work independently.	Authority and control.	Give them information quickly so they can make a rapid decision.
Thinker	Task-oriented people who are methodical and thoughtful about the details of a project or task. They tend to like tasks that are complex.	They do things very carefully and analyze everything. They decide on a course of action after they have had time to thoroughly think about the issues involved.	Accuracy and precision.	Approach them in a nonthreatening manner. Give them time to gather information and be deliberate in their decision-making.
Socializer	People-oriented people who seek approval from others. They like to be spontaneous and are very expressive.	They often have ideas and they use their communication skills to get others to work with them.	Popularity and appearances.	Provide them with information and allow them to make it clear that the decision is collaborative in nature.
Relater	People-oriented people who seek stability and security. They enjoy being a part of a team and want to know the details of any plans, tasks, or projects.	They are very diplomatic and they find methods to come to solutions.	Affiliation and stability.	Provide them with information and ask them for their opinion.

Source: Adapted from Coaching for Results (Online program). Boston: Harvard Business School Publishing; 2000.

When workplace conflicts arise, managers often have to intervene to resolve the situation. Some techniques you can use include:

- Lead by example. Don't raise your voice and be aware of nonverbal communication.

- Don't make the conflict personal. Avoid using the word "I" and use real examples that have been observed.

- Focus on dealing with the situation and not the individual characteristics of the people involved in the conflict.

- Address the issue quickly; do not let it continue or get worse.

- Ask all involved in the conflict to summarize their views regarding the issues.

- Set a reasonable deadline for those involved to propose solutions. Be sure to stick to the established deadline.

- Explore and discuss solutions and commit to making the changes necessary to resolve the conflict.

- Make a decision and explain the decision to the people involved.

- Re-evaluate the decision at a predetermined time in the future.

- Learn from conflict; it can be an opportunity for growth.

- If the conflict reoccurs, investigate the root cause and implement corrective action as soon as possible.

Terminating an Employee

One of the most unfortunate and unpleasant experiences a pharmacy manager may face is to terminate an employee. It is, however, a reality that you'll probably have to deal with at some point during your career. Terminating an employee may be the only course of action for a variety of reasons, such as when the employee:

- Consistently fails to perform required tasks and meet job expectations.

- Grossly violates rules in the pharmacy's code of conduct or employee manual, such as threatening violence or committing a violent act.

- Engages in illegal conduct, such as stealing or diverting medications.

Documentation

Regardless of the reason for the termination, you must ensure that you have proper documentation and background available regarding the termination. In some cases, you may want to review this material with your direct supervisor or legal counsel before the termination to ensure that all aspects are covered. This documentation might include notes about oral warnings, copies of written warnings and suspensions, or acknowledgments of company policy on expected behavior and rules.

Immediate Dismissal

Sometimes employees must be terminated immediately because they directly violated the pharmacy's code of conduct or were involved in illegal acts. Steps to consider when faced with a situation that calls for immediate termination:

- Ensure that the employee is not a danger to himself or herself or to other employees.

  - If the employee appears to be a danger, help the others to safety and call law enforcement authorities or security immediately.

  - If the employee does not appear to be a danger, contact law enforcement authorities if an illegal act has occurred.

- Remain polite and respectful.

- With a witness in the room, calmly inform the employee of the offense.

- Tell the employee that his or her employment is terminated.

- Obtain all company property from the employee.

- Allow the employee to gather personal items.

- Allow the employee to ask any questions regarding the end of his or her employment.

- Escort the former employee from the premises with the understanding that he or she should not return; if the person returns, it will be considered trespassing.

Table 3-5 covers steps to follow when terminating an employee for not meeting performance expectations.

Table 3-5 | Terminating an Employee for Lack of Job Performance

Before the Termination Meeting	During the Termination Meeting	After the Termination Meeting
Ensure that the employee was made aware of job expectations.	Schedule the meeting to include the employee, the employee's direct supervisor (which may be the pharmacy manager), and a witness. (Suggestions include a member of human resources, a mid- or upper-level manager, or another member of management in the organization.)	Notify the Human Resources Department or person responsible for employee status of the termination so that records are updated in a timely manner and applicable information regarding benefits is sent to the employee.
If policies and procedures are not being followed, ensure that they are written and that the employee was trained properly in this area.	Be civil, concise, and straightforward as you inform the employee that his or her job is terminated. Explain to the employee the reasons for the termination. Be compassionate.	Notify the network administrator or other appropriate people to disable the former employee's access to computer, telephone, alarm, pharmacy site, etc.
Determine that performance standards are being applied consistently and fairly to everyone in the pharmacy.	Allow the employee to ask any questions he or she may have regarding the termination and next steps. Do not become angry if the employee brings a hostile or negative tone to the conversation.	Determine how best to communicate the employee's termination to the other pharmacy team members.
In progressive discipline, each written document involving the employee's performance must escalate so that oral warnings, written warnings, and suspensions (if applicable) are on record. This ensures that the employment termination is not a surprise to the employee.	Give the employee feedback about the types of positions he or she may want to consider pursuing in the future. Provide information regarding the person's strengths and potential sources for future employment.	

Supporting a Satisfying Workplace

This chapter gives just a brief overview of personnel issues you will deal with regularly as a pharmacy manager. A big chunk of your responsibilities will have to do with managing your staff, dealing with performance, and tackling challenges related to HR. Good managers are aware of their employees' issues and concerns, stay on top of labor laws and trends, and promote an efficient, satisfying environment for everyone in their pharmacy practice.

Jennifer Brandt, PharmD
Clinical Specialist Pharmacist in Critical Care and Clinical Resource Utilization
Washington Hospital Center

Q: What is your professional pharmacy background?

I graduated from the University of Rhode Island College of Pharmacy in 2002 with my PharmD. I went on to complete a PGY-1 general practice residency at the Washington Hospital Center, a 926-bed tertiary care teaching hospital and level 1 trauma center in Washington, DC. After completing my residency, I became a clinical pharmacist in critical care, eventually moving up the career ladder to my current position, which I have held for four years.

I'm a clinical pharmacist covering the burn and trauma intensive care unit and step-down units. I also oversee the Drug Information Center, serve as a preceptor for our pharmacy residents, and am responsible for much of the material presented at the Pharmacy and Therapeutics (P&T) Committee, including clinical practice guidelines, therapeutic interchanges, formulary reviews, and drug use evaluations. Other responsibilities include serving on the hospital Emergency Preparedness Committee, co-chairing the corporate Clinical Pharmacist Workgroup, and serving on the corporate P&T Committee.

Q: Talk about your involvement in professional organizations.

I have been a member of the American Society of Health-System Pharmacists (ASHP) since college and have had opportunities to work on advisory panels addressing emergency preparedness and pandemic influenza. Recently, I was selected to participate in the ASHP Pharmacy Practice Model Initiative summit. I also serve on a special advisory group for the same initiative.

Since college I've been involved in Lambda Kappa Sigma (LKS), a professional pharmacy fraternity. Right now I'm the LKS grand treasurer, and I've served as the LKS grand vice president for alumni and regional supervisor. I'm an active member of the Society of Critical Care Medicine and the American Burn Association, serving on the Committee for the Organized Delivery of Burn Care.

Q: What's your advice for a student or staff pharmacist with the goal of being a pharmacy manager?

Take every opportunity to ask questions and learn. Find someone in a managerial role and ask him or her to be a mentor.

I have learned a great deal from my director of pharmacy on topics from finance to operations to personnel management. I only needed to let him know that I was interested.

Also, get involved in school organizations. Taking the role of an officer or committee chair can give you early experience managing both people and projects.

Q: What prepared you to take a pharmacy manager position?

The mentoring sessions I have had with my director have set the stage for me to take a leadership role in my department. Also, through organizational work I've learned how to deal with differing personalities and issues. I frequently find myself applying lessons learned in one setting to another.

Also, I've never turned down an opportunity, whether it is taking the lead on a project, chairing a committee, or participating in a class or conference. I'm currently participating in the Pharmacy Leadership Academy through ASHP to continue to learn about all aspects of leadership.

Q: What challenges did you have as a new pharmacy manager?

My age has been my biggest challenge. I ascended the career ladder fairly quickly, and so I'm younger than many staff who fall below me in the organizational hierarchy. Some resent that I seemed to gain my position so easily, even though it took a lot of hard work and initiative. Others refuse to listen to me or give the same credibility to my ideas that they do for my older counterparts. I deal with this by continuing to do high-quality work so I prove my worth to them over time, which has worked in many instances.

Q: What benefits or rewards have you experienced as a new pharmacy manager?

The biggest benefit has been recognition for my work. I now know that my work has a huge impact on the organization and the corporation. It is a great source of pride for me when I see put in place an initiative or guideline I've worked on.

Q: How have networking, having a mentor, or involvement in professional associations helped your development as a pharmacy manager?

I am lucky to have a very open relationship with my mentor—my director. I have been able to ask questions that help me continue to learn, and he has provided me with opportunities I wouldn't have had otherwise because I've worked hard and prepared myself—such as serving on advisory boards, presenting at national meetings, and even appearing on National Public Radio.

The organizations I belong to have also helped me learn how to work with others, lead all types of people, and collaborate with leaders in the field. Now I have friends in varying positions all across the country whose leadership styles I've been able to watch and incorporate into my own.

Q: From your perspective, what are the attributes of a manager and a leader?

Management and leadership have big differences, but the two often go hand in hand. Management deals with solving daily problems and issues—which may involve writing policies and procedures or other practical approaches. Leadership, however, involves thinking ahead and thinking outside the box to bring about progress.

Both managers and leaders must be good communicators and problem solvers. If a leader cannot communicate his or her vision to followers, the vision will fail.

Marc Summerfield, RPh, MS

Senior Director of Pharmacy
University of Maryland Medical Center

Q: What is your professional pharmacy background?

I have been a pharmacy manager for 35 years and I've worked at the University of Maryland Medical Center for 10 years. In my current position I direct inpatient and outpatient pharmacy services for a 705-bed tertiary care teaching hospital in Baltimore. The pharmacy department provides a full range of contemporary pharmacy services to the medical center's patients and employees.

Although born in Cheverly, Maryland, I grew up in a small seashore town outside of Asbury Park, New Jersey. After graduating from the University of Connecticut School of Pharmacy in 1974, I moved to Baltimore and completed a joint two-year program: a residency in hospital pharmacy at The Johns Hopkins Hospital and Master of Science in institutional pharmacy at the University of Maryland. Then I spent two years as supervisor of the Oncology Pharmacy at The Johns Hopkins Hospital.

For most of my career I was a pediatric pharmacy manager. My first director's job was at the Arkansas Children's Hospital, a stand-alone pediatric facility in Little Rock affiliated with the University of Arkansas for Medical Sciences. I then served as the first director of pharmacy at the Texas Children's Hospital in Houston. A major achievement in both institutions was implementing a computerized system that delivers medications in unit-dose form in a patient-specific, dose-specific, time-specific envelope—one envelope per dose, no more than eight hours before scheduled administration time. The envelopes were sorted by patient care unit, then scheduled time of administration, then patient. Both systems operate today.

Q: What's your advice for a student or staff pharmacist who wants to be a pharmacy manager?

Read, attend classes, lectures, and seminars, observe, and think. You have to develop the mind-set, thinking patterns, and aura of a manager and leader—which takes preparation and practice over many years, and of course, is never done. But first, you have to accept the responsibilities, including the time, anxiety, and effort that accompany the perks. Be sure you want to "do" the job and not just "be" the job. The glamour of the promotion and title wears off quickly, leaving the essential functions, which one can enjoy or detest.

Q: How did you prepare to be a pharmacy manager?

My residency program and graduate work set the wheels in motion. My residency director and major professor started me on the path of acting and thinking as a manager and leader. They stressed the importance of constant learning, of developing problem-solving skills, and of building good communication skills—writing even more than speaking. Overcoming the program's challenges and trials gave me the confidence to embark on the management/leadership journey.

Q: What challenges did you face as a new manager?

I distinctly recall my main challenge was working with older pharmacists and technicians. I felt awkward performing the basic personnel functions: directing, controlling, interviewing, and counseling. It's much easier to do these things now with someone who could be my daughter or grandson than it was with someone who could be my mother or grandfather.

One other early challenge, which I still struggle with, is the ability to be simultaneously firm but pleasant. I found myself being aggressive (firm but unpleasant) or pliable (weak but pleasant). And I struggled with the challenge of advocating for my beliefs and principles without alienating others.

Q: How have networking, having a mentor, or involvement in professional associations helped your development as a pharmacy manager?

Networking is a critical component of being an effective manager and leader. Establishing relationships external to the organization fuels progress—conceptually and functionally.

I believe the key attribute of a manager is the ability to make decisions that are resolute and timely. A manager must be decisive—but not arbitrary and not necessarily deciding without input or research. Leaders must have a vision for themselves and their unit, the internal confidence to pursue the vision, and the propensity to act. I admire the word "propensity" because it implies a tendency that is careful, calculated, timely, and definite, and it dispels any notion of foolhardiness and irresponsibility.

Q: What principles guide you?

One of my guiding principles is to focus on employees. "Employees?" you say, "employees? Are we not here for the patients?" Of course, but as a leader and manager, I don't interact with patients directly, so my contribution to care is how I impact the employees who do interact directly.

My triad for employee-centered leadership is "connection," "gratitude," and "responsiveness." Employees need to know that they are connected with their leaders, that the leaders appreciate and recognize what they do, and that the leaders are responsive to their ideas and needs.

Exercise 3-1 | New Employee Orientation Checklist

(Use the blank lines for additional items)			
☑	Item	☑	Item
	Employee Handbook (or similar document)		
	Review of Key Company Policies		
	Anti-harassment policy		Employee conduct standards
	Confidentiality (including HIPAA)		Vacation and sick leave
	Security		Holidays
	Email and Internet usage		Performance reviews
	Dress code		Progressive disciplinary actions
	Introduction and Tours		
	Pharmacy Department staff		Administrative supplies
	Front store or other company/ institution staff (if applicable)		Kitchen/break room
	Facility tour		Emergency exits
	Restrooms		Parking
	Pharmacy Department Orientation		
	Introduction to team and staff		Review job schedule and hours
	Review initial job assignments and training plans		Review payroll timing, recording work time, policies and procedures
	Review job description and performance expectations and standards		

continued on page 98

Exercise 3-1 | New Employee Orientation Checklist, *continued*

(Use the blank lines for additional items)			
☑	Item	☑	Item
	Organization Orientation		
	Follow-up Orientation Plan		
	Provide employee with follow-up meeting schedule		
	Additional Items		

Exercise 3-2 | Monitoring Staff Motivation

Complete this chart quarterly to keep track of the motivation level of your staff and to monitor how well you are using available strategies to keep them motivated.
Date:
Staff Morale is (Up? Down? Flat? Mixed?) because
Success or major milestones the team has achieved thus far:
Team members who have been instrumental in successes to date and what motivates them:
Reward methods and ideas for the team:
Aspects to emphasize to the team (i.e., vision, specific objectives, and goals):

Exercise 3-3 | **Checklist for Delegation Skills**

Use this checklist to observe how well you delegate.		
Question	**Yes**	**No**
1. Do you spend most of your time completing tasks that require your specific level of skill, knowledge, and authority?		
2. Do your team members know what you expect of them?		
3. Do you feel comfortable sharing control with your staff?		
4. Do you have trust and confidence in the ability of your team members to complete their assignments successfully?		
5. Do you assign tasks that can be done by others to the appropriate possible staff level?		
6. Do you clearly outline the expected results from a delegated task/assignment/project and hold the staff member(s) accountable for achieving these results?		
7. Do you take the time to carefully select the right person for the right job?		
8. Do you support your staff with an appropriate level of feedback and follow-up?		
9. Do you focus on the results achieved versus the method/process used to achieve results?		
10. Do you allow your team members sufficient time to solve their own problems before you provide advice?		
If you answer "yes" to six or more questions, you are doing a good job of delegating. For those questions to which you answer "no," identify how you can change your behaviors and practices to improve on how you delegate a task or project.		

Additional Resources

- *1001 Ways to Energize Employees.* Nelson B, Morris B, Blanchard K. New York: Workman Publishing Company; 1997. This reference provides information on the methods and techniques that successful American companies are using to engage their employees.

- *The Art of Giving and Receiving Feedback.* Massetti Miller KM, Poertner S. West Des Moines, Iowa: American Media; 1996. A how-to guide regarding feedback, this reference provides managers with self-assessment and goal-setting activities to better prepare for feedback and other managerial responsibilities.

- *Coaching and Counseling: A Practical Guide for Managers and Team Leaders (50-Minute Series).* 3rd ed. Minor M. Menlo Park, Calif: Crisp Publications; 2002. This reference covers coaching and counseling, including understanding the characteristics of effective coaches and counselors, methods for giving and receiving feedback, and tips for developing an action plan to develop and refine skills for motivating, coaching, and counseling employees.

- *Delegating for Results (50-Minute Series).* 2nd ed. Maddux RB. Boston: Crisp Publications; 1998. This reference explores manager delegation issues, including removing barriers to delegation, using levels of authority, and working through issues related to why managers choose not to delegate.

- *Firing Without Fear: A Legal Guide for Conscientious Employers.* Repa BK. Berkeley, Calif: Nolo; 2000. This guide looks at elements managers should be knowledgeable about regarding employee termination, including progressive discipline, the termination process, and the laws, myths, and realities of termination.

- *Goals and Goal-Setting: Planning to Succeed (50-Minute Series).* 2nd ed. Rouillard LA. Menlo Park, Calif: Crisp Publications; 1998. This reference defines goals, missions, and objectives and well as the process for setting, identifying, documenting, developing, and reviewing goals.

- *Handling the Difficult Employee: A Practical Guide for Managers (50-Minute Series).* Brounstein M. Menlo Park, Calif: Crisp Publications; 1993. This reference describes how to identify the difficult employee and presents a six-step intervention model, giving constructive feedback and using a progressive discipline policy.

continued

- **Influencing and Motivating Others.** Online Program. Boston: Harvard Business School Publishing; 2001. This online interactive course provides challenging, dialogue-based scenarios where the choices made drive the conversation and results. You come away with tools for getting better results from direct reports, greater cooperation from peers, and stronger support from supervisors and upper management.

- **The Management Guide to Delegating.** Keenan K. Horsham, West Sussex: Ravette Publishing; 1996. This reference is part of The Management Guide series that discusses the importance of and process for delegating.

- **Painless Performance Evaluations: A Practical Approach to Managing Day-to-Day Employee Performance.** Green ME. Upper Saddle River, NJ: Prentice Hall; 2005. This guide to conducting performance evaluations discusses duties associated with managing performance, including improving employee communication and documenting employee performance.

- **The ROI of Human Capital: Measuring the Economic Value of Employee Performance.** 2nd ed. Fitz-enz J. New York: AMACOM; 2009. This reference describes the value of human productivity in an organization, the concept of measuring the return on investment (ROI) of a company based on human productivity, and how organizations can improve their value through elements that impact human productivity.

- **Society for Human Resource Management**: www.shrm.org. The official website for the Society for Human Resource Management, the largest association devoted to human resource management, provides many free resources and articles pertinent to effective employee management. It also offers information about programs available for human resource professionals that managers can attend for additional information and training.

- **Taking the Stress Out of Stressful Conversations. Harvard Business Review OnPoint Enhanced Edition.** Weeks H. Boston: Harvard Business School Publishing; March 2002. This reference provides insight into the process and qualities managers should be aware of regarding stressful conversations in the workplace, including how managers can improve interactions through greater self-awareness, rehearsal, and preparation.

References

1. Scott DM, Narducci WA, Jungnickel PW, et al. Pharmaceutical care preceptor training and assessment in community pharmacy clerkship sites. *Am J Pharm Educ.* 1999;63:265–71.

2. Accreditation Standards and Guidelines for the Professional Program in Pharmacy Leading to the Doctor of Pharmacy Degree. Adopted January 15, 2006. Available at: http://www.acpe-accredit.org/pdf/ACPE_Revised_PharmD_Standards_Adopted_Jan152006.pdf. Accessed April 25, 2011.

3. Lee CD, Bradley-Baker LR. Successful recruitment and hiring strategies. In: Chisholm-Burns MA, Vaillancourt AM, Shepherd M, eds. *Pharmacy Management, Leadership, Marketing, and Finance.* Sudbury, Mass: Jones and Bartlett; 2010:187–214.

4. Steingold FS. *The Employer's Legal Handbook.* 8th ed. Berkeley, Calif: Nolo; 2007.

5. Arthur D. The *Employee Recruitment and Retention Handbook.* New York: AMACOM; 2001.

6. Wick J. Supervision of pharmacy personnel. *J Am Pharm Assoc.* 1998;38(4):457–68.

7. Gotkin V, Ross LA. Employment law essentials. In: Chisholm-Burns MA, Vaillancourt AM, Shepherd M, eds. *Pharmacy Management, Leadership, Marketing, and Finance.* Sudbury, Mass: Jones and Bartlett; 2010:335–49.

8. Wick JY. *Supervision: A Pharmacy Perspective.* Washington, DC: American Pharmacists Association; 2003:11–14.

9. Employee relations. In: *Society for Human Resource Management (SHRM) Human Resource (HR) Generalist Program Manual.* Washington, DC: Society for Human Resource Management; 2008:149–67.

10. Maddux RB. *Delegating for Results.* Menlo Park, Calif: Crisp Publications; 1990:7–8.

11. *Coaching Collection.* Harvard Business Review Collection. Boston: Harvard Business School Publishing; 1997.

12. McDonough RP, Pezzullo LM. *What No One Ever Told You about Pharmacy Management.* Podium presentation at: Annual Meeting of the American Pharmacists Association, March 2010; Washington, DC.

13. *The Manager's Guide to Negotiation and Conflict Resolution. Harvard Management Communication Letter Collection.* Boston: Harvard Business School Publishing; 2000.

Chapter 4

Financial Aspects of Pharmacy Management

Understanding the Basics

All pharmacy managers must have a full understanding of how to maintain the economic health of their pharmacy practice as well as how to improve its financial performance. Being well grounded in accounting principles, inventory management, and budgeting will help you keep your pharmacy on track and operating smoothly.

Accounting in Pharmacy Management

In pharmacy practice, the basis of managing finances is fundamental accounting—a discipline that involves selecting, collecting, arranging, and reporting the flow of financial information within a business.[1] Accounting allows you to understand how the flow of revenue—or money—is tracked in your pharmacy practice. All organizations use accounting information to facilitate financial decision-making.[2]

The essence of a pharmacy manager's job is making decisions, many of which have financial implications. This chapter will provide information on the following:

- Accounting basics

- Inventory

- Budget considerations

Pharmacies simply can't do without an accounting system—the set of procedures and controls used to identify relevant transactions and events within the pharmacy.[3] Accounting systems provide source documents and financial statements that reflect the pharmacy's economic outcomes. The box on page 104 covers some basic accounting principles.

Basic Accounting Principles

- Accounting entries should be recorded on the basis of objective evidence.

- Accounting estimates, evaluations, and opinions should be fair and reasonable so that decisions will not be made from financial statements that were unrealistically prepared.

- Transactions are the basic economic exchanges between two entities. Each transaction must be recorded separately. Each transaction will affect the asset (items owned) and liability (debts) accounts, and some will affect equity accounts (amount remaining after liabilities are subtracted from assets).

- In accrual accounting, revenue and expenses are recorded in the time frame in which they are earned or incurred, regardless of whether cash is received.

- In cash basis accounting, revenue and expenses are recorded in the period during which they are actually received or spent.

- The "Accounting Equation" describes the relationship between assets, liabilities, and owner's equity:

  Assets = Liabilities + Owner's Equity

- All expenses directly associated with producing revenues must be reported within the same period on the income (profit-and-loss) statement.

Source: Adapted from Mosavin R. Financial reports. In: Desselle SP, Zgarrick DP, eds. *Pharmacy Management: Essentials for All Practice Settings.* McGraw-Hill Companies; 2009:247–63.

A financial statement is a written report that quantitatively describes a company's financial status. Financial statements work in concert with other information, such as the state of the national and local economy, the demand for a product or service, or the loyalty of employees and patients, to provide a fiscal picture of a pharmacy. The four financial statements used by most companies are:

- Balance sheet.

- Income statement.

- Statement of retained earnings.

- Statement of cash flows.

The Balance Sheet

The balance sheet presents the pharmacy's present financial status. This itemized statement displays total assets and total liabilities and provides the value of a company's net worth at any specific time, including what the company owns and owes.[3] The fundamental balance sheet equation is:

$$Assets = Liabilities + Owners' Equity$$

Assets

Assets are items an individual or company owns that have some type of value. Examples of assets in a pharmacy setting include:

- Accounts receivable: amounts owed to the pharmacy by its customers as a result of ordinary extension of credit.

- Cash and cash equivalents.

- Inventory: includes both merchandise and supplies.

- Property and equipment: includes items such as computers, software, registers, fixtures, cars, land, and buildings.

Liabilities

Liabilities are the debts of a business, made up of the assets, products, or services a company is obligated to make payments on because of past transactions or events. Examples of liabilities in a pharmacy practice include:

- Accounts payable: debts from purchasing goods or services on credit. In pharmacy, most of these debts come from purchasing merchandise inventory.

- Advertising.

- Depreciation.

- Insurance.

- Legal and accounting expenses.

- Payroll.

- Rent.

- Utilities.

Owner's Equity

Owners' equity is the amount remaining after liabilities are subtracted from assets. Owners' equity is also known as net worth, stockholders' equity, or capital.

> Being well grounded in accounting principles, inventory management, and budgeting will help you keep your pharmacy on track.

The Income Statement

The income statement, also known as the profit and loss statement, provides the revenues, expenses, and net income of a business for a specific period of time—whether a month, a quarter, or a year.[1] The basic income statement equation is:

$$\text{Revenues} - \text{Expenses} = \text{Net Income}$$

Revenue

Revenue is a form of an asset that produces a gross increase in equity from business activities resulting in income or sales. Most sales in pharmacy practice are generated from selling prescription and over-the-counter drugs, other nonprescription items such as health and beauty aids, and professional services and programs. Revenue is generated through cash and credit sales.

Expenses

Expenses are costs the pharmacy incurs to make sales or earn revenues. Table 4-1 lists expenses that contribute to the overall cost of operating a pharmacy. Controllable or variable expenses are costs for which management can decide the amount to pay out, while noncontrollable expenses are costs that are not subject to management's influence.

Payroll for pharmacy personnel tends to make up the largest share of pharmacy expenses. Payment not only includes wages but also employee benefits such as medical benefits, workers' compensation insurance, financial plan contributions, taxes for unemployment and Federal Insurance Contributions Act (also known as Social Security), vacation pay, and holiday pay, if applicable.

Table 4-1 | Pharmacy Expenses

Controllable Expenses	Noncontrollable Expenses
Bank charges	Advertising
Utilities	Rent
Credit card fees	Taxes and licenses
Inventory services	Insurance
Telephone	Depreciation
Repairs, maintenance, janitorial	Leased equipment
Security	Payroll
Supplies	

Source: Adapted from Herist KN, Wade WE. Cents and sensibility: Understanding the numbers. In: Chisholm-Burns MA, Vaillancourt AM, Shepherd M, eds. *Pharmacy Management, Leadership, Marketing, and Finance.* Sudbury, Mass: Jones and Bartlett; 2010:187–214.

Net Income

Net income is the difference between revenues and expenses for a specific period of time. Net income is also known as net profit or earnings.

Statement of Retained Earnings

The statement of retained earnings, also known as the statement of owner's equity, provides information on how the earnings of a business have changed over a period of time. The statement displays the amount of retained earnings at the beginning of the period and the major changes to retained earnings over that period. Included are dividend payments or net losses (which decrease retained earnings) and the net income and additional owner investments (which increase retained earnings).

Statement of Cash Flows

The statement of cash flows, also known as the sources and uses statement or statement of changes in financial position, provides detailed information on how a pharmacy obtained cash during a certain time period and how it used that cash. Although the balance sheet and income statement use the accrual basis of accounting, the statement of cash flows uses the cash basis of accounting.

The statement of cash flows provides an accurate picture to evaluate how well a pharmacy's cash is managed and the pharmacy's ability to generate sufficient cash flow to meet its financial responsibilities.

Ratio Analysis

Ratio analysis provides additional information about a company's performance. By converting the financial numbers of a company into ratios, or performing ratio analyses, you can make comparisons between a company's historical performance and its expected performance.[4]

The three common types of ratios used in pharmacy are:

- Solvency—evaluates a company's long-term ability to meet all financial obligations.

- Liquidity—evaluates a company's short-term ability to meet all financial obligations.

- Profitability—measures the company's ability to make money.

Table 4-2 gives a quick overview of commonly used ratio analyses for financial management in pharmacy.

Table 4-2 | Ratio Analyses Used in Pharmacy Management

Name of Ratio	Ratio Measurement	Ratio Is Used to...
Acid-Test Ratio	Quick Assets + Current Liabilities	indicate instant debt-paying ability.
Current Ratio	Current Assets + Current Liabilities	determine a company's ability to pay short-term obligations.

Table 4-2 | *continued*

Debt Ratio	Total Debt ÷ Total Assets	indicate the proportion of debt that a company has relative to its assets.
Debt to Equity Ratio	Total Liabilities ÷ Shareholders Equity	measure a company's financial leverage by indicating the proportion of equity and debt the company uses to finance its assets.
Gross Margin Ratio (%)	Revenue − Cost of Goods Sold/Revenue	represent the proportion of each dollar of revenue that a company retains as gross margin.
Return on Investment	(Gain from Investment − Cost of Investment)/Cost of Investment	measure performance to evaluate the efficiency of an investment.
Working Capital	Current Assets − Current Liabilities	indicate the ability to meet current maturing obligations.
Accounts Receivable	Net Sales on Account + Average Accounts Receivable	assess the efficiency in collecting receivables and in managing credit.
Average Prescription Sales Price	Total Prescription Sales ÷ Number of Prescriptions Dispensed	obtain information on the relative mix of medications dispensed by the pharmacy.
Generic Prescription Percent	Cost of Goods Sold of Generic Medications Dispensed ÷ Cost of Goods Sold of Total Medications Dispensed	obtain information on the efficiency of dispensing generic medications. Generic medications provide a greater margin or profit than brand-name medications.
Inventory Turnover	Cost of Goods Sold + Average Inventory	assess the efficiency in the management of inventory.
Third-Party Percent	Number of Prescriptions paid by Third Parties ÷ Total Amount of Prescriptions	indicate the portion of prescriptions subsidized by a third-party plan. Third-party prescriptions usually have a lower gross margin or profit than cash prescriptions.

Source: Adapted from the following:
Herist KN, Wade WE. Cents and sensibility: Understanding the numbers. In: Chisholm-Burns MA, Vaillancourt AM, Shepherd M, eds. *Pharmacy Management, Leadership, Marketing, and Finance.* Sudbury, Mass: Jones and Bartlett; 2010:187–214.

Financial Statement Analysis. In: Carroll NV, ed. *Financial Management for Pharmacists: A Decision-Making Approach.* 3rd ed. Baltimore: Lippincott Williams & Wilkins; 2007:53–71.

Inventory in Pharmacy Management

Effectively managing inventory in the pharmacy is key to ensuring the pharmacy's profitability. Inventory control involves the optimal level of procurement, care, and dispensing or selling of products in a pharmacy setting. This is important for a number of reasons, including:

- Maintaining an accurate level of products for patients and customers and meeting market demands.

- Reducing the level of costs associated with carrying and holding products.

- Improving the rate of inventory turnover.

- Building the pharmacy's reputation for always having the products needed and requested by patients, customers, and health care prescribers.

Merchandise inventory is often a pharmacy's largest asset. Cost of goods sold—that is, the cost of merchandise that the pharmacy sold during the year—is an expense. When doing accounting for inventory and cost of goods sold, two important things to consider are:

- The system used to measure inventory and cost of goods sold.

- How inventory and cost of goods sold are calculated when prices change over the accounting period.

Systems for Measurement

Inventory and cost of goods sold can be measured using one of two systems:

- The periodic system

- The perpetual system

Because conducting a physical inventory is costly, most pharmacies go through the process only once a year, regardless of the inventory management system they use.

Effectively managing inventory in the pharmacy is key to ensuring the pharmacy's profitability.

Periodic System

In the periodic system of inventory, you can perform a physical inventory count at specific intervals. You record merchandise purchases in the "purchases" account and do not make adjustments to the inventory account for either sales or purchases.

In the periodic system, the cost of goods sold is measured using the formula below, after you conduct a physical inventory of the pharmacy:

Cost of goods sold = Beginning Inventory + Purchases − Ending Inventory

Perpetual System

In the perpetual system of measurement, you maintain current and accurate accounts for inventory and cost of goods sold by constantly updating the balances in these accounts. Most pharmacies, especially those with a computerized system for maintaining inventory levels, use the perpetual system, which can provide information on the cost of goods anytime without conducting a physical inventory.

Pharmacies have to determine how they assign costs to their inventory, because merchandise costs usually change over the course of a year. Costs can be assigned to inventory in a variety of ways:

1. Weighted average cost method, which provides a cost that represents the product's cost over the entire accounting period.

2. First-in, first-out method, which assumes that the first units bought are the first ones sold.

3. Last-in, first-out method, which assumes that the last units bought are the first ones sold.

Measuring "Shrink"

A physical inventory provides the necessary information to measure "shrink"—that is, the amount of inventory that is lost from the pharmacy. You calculate shrink by comparing the inventory level recorded in the inventory account with the amounts you find when doing a physical inventory. Shrink, which can adversely affect the pharmacy profitability, can be present in a pharmacy setting for a number of reasons, including:

- External theft of merchandise by shoplifters or other people outside of the pharmacy staff. Video surveillance, other mechanical tools, and providing friendly service to everyone who visits the pharmacy can help deter external theft.

- Internal theft of merchandise by pharmacy employees. Suggested deterrents for internal theft include checking references and conducting a criminal background check during the hiring process, not allowing employees to ring up their own purchases, having a management member inspect bags when employee shifts are completed, and not allowing personal belongings such as purses and coats in the pharmacy area during scheduled shifts.

- Administrative issues such as incorrectly processing prescriptions, incorrectly ringing up prescriptions, being charged incorrectly for orders placed with internal or outside vendors, inaccurate inventory management record-keeping, and incorrect practices involving other systems where purchases and credits are tracked. Setting up a system to efficiently and correctly track purchases and credits and physically inspecting vendor orders can greatly assist in reducing pharmacy paperwork errors.

Additional information regarding inventory management is provided in the box on page 113.

General Guidelines for Managing Inventory

1. Review inventory levels a minimum of once a quarter to adjust for seasonal trends.

2. Have pharmacy staff develop a system for returning outdated or overstock medications for credit on a regular basis, such as monthly.

3. Refrain from ordering expensive items to sit in current inventory. Ask patients who use such medications to contact the pharmacy a week before they need a refill and order at that time.

4. Closely monitor order cycle times for merchandise deliveries to limit potential overstock or out-of-stock situations in the pharmacy.

5. Use next-day delivery of merchandise, if available, to meet the inventory needs of your clients and lower inventory costs.

Budgeting

A time may come in your career as a pharmacy manager when you are an integral participant in developing the budget for your practice setting. Each organization has its own process of budget development, implementation, and tracking, but the basic elements of budgeting are universal.

A budget is a tool for forecasting events as part of the planning process for the future.[2] It describes the pharmacy's objectives and functional plans in monetary terms. Budgetary accounting allows for planning and controlling business operations by measuring the cost of planned acquisitions and the use of economic resources in the future. Various types of budgets used in pharmacy settings are described in Table 4-3.

> A budget is a tool for forecasting events as part of the planning process for the future.

Table 4-3 | **Types of Budget in a Pharmacy Practice Setting**

Name of Budget	Description of Budget
Capital Budget	Projects the estimated amounts planned for capital assets in a given period. It consists of only the current-year expenditures.
Cash Budget	Displays a company's cash flow for the period (normally 12 months) and is derived from information found in the operating budget.
Operating Budget	An itemized listing of the amount of all estimated revenue that an organization anticipates receiving, along with a listing of the amount of all estimated costs and expenses that will be earned in reaching the budgeted income during a given period (which is typically one business cycle or year). This is also known as a forecasted income statement.
Operating Expense Budget	Projects the estimated expenses for the forecast period.
Zero-Based Budget	Builds a budget from zero; the budget planners ignore the revenues, expenses, or cost of the prior period's performance when establishing the future period's performance.

Source: Adapted from Herist KN, Wade WE. Cents and sensibility: Understanding the numbers. In: Chisholm-Burns MA, Vaillancourt AM, Shepherd M, eds. *Pharmacy Management, Leadership, Marketing, and Finance.* Sudbury, Mass: Jones and Bartlett; 2010:187–214.

Why Have a Budget?

Budgets are developed and used for the following reasons.[2]

1. Planning—provides pharmacy managers and their staff with specific goals for their department or for initiatives within the department.

2. Supporting communication and coordination—ensures that procedures are established and followed so the budget can be controlled.

3. Assigning resources—ensures that the necessary allocations of current and future assets are decided on in concordance with budgetary considerations.

4. Benchmarking—allows pharmacy managers to compare the success of budgetary control in the areas for which they are financially responsible as well as compared with other departments and organizations.

5. Assessing performance—enables a pharmacy manager's performance to be evaluated, in part, by his or her ability to increase revenue while controlling expenses.

Forecasting

Forecasting is the first and most important step in preparing a budget for a pharmacy.[2] A forecast is an estimate of demand for the next 6 to 12 months. The demand being measured will change according to the type of budget being developed as well as by the type of pharmacy setting. For example, in community pharmacy, a demand used for budgeting is a sales forecast, while in hospital pharmacy, a demand is patient admissions.

Among the many methods that organizations use to develop their budgets are:

- Forecasting for an existing pharmacy.

- Replicating the prior year's budget without any changes.

- Using the actual performance of the current period to forecast the next year's budget.

- Using the actual performance of the prior year with an anticipated percentage increase, decrease, or no change in each line item based on certain assumptions or goals set by the management. This is the method most commonly used.

- Forecasting for a new pharmacy.

- Developing an estimate of market potential using published statistics on area demand, local census data, prescription usage, and price statistics.[5,6,7]

- Establishing future period performance with justification for all budget line items without ignoring prior period revenues, expenses, or costs.

In addition to previous performance, forecasting should consider the following attributes:

- Changes in competition.

- Business conditions.

- Economic conditions.

- Government regulation.

- Pharmacy marketing programs.

- New methods of treatment.

- Changes in prices, promotion, service, hours of operations, and products.

Planning

Planning, which is a critical activity in the budget process, entails identifying what the organization expects to accomplish and how it intends to accomplish it. The planning process starts from a global perspective—pinpointing the organization's goals—and narrows down to intricate details, which include planning the budget.

Below are the steps in planning organizational goals that lay the groundwork for an accurate budget.[8] Most pharmacies don't go through this planning process every year; more likely, it takes place when the pharmacy initially opens or when a major expansion or revision of services is expected.

1. Examining the organization's mission statement. A mission statement is a broad, general description of the basic societal need that the organization seeks to accomplish. For example, "The mission of Friendly Care Pharmacy is to provide the most competent, extraordinary, accessible, and caring pharmacy services to the patients in our surrounding community."

2. Define the goals of the organization. Goals are the end points that must be accomplished so the organization can fulfill its mission. For example, two goals of Friendly Care Pharmacy based on the mission may be:

- Provide medication therapy management services to all patients taking more than three medications.

- Provide mechanisms to assist patients to afford their prescribed medications.

3. Establish the strategies to be employed to reach the organization's goals. In this step, you develop broad guidelines that can be used to meet the end points defined in step 2. For example, for the first goal above, you might contact by various means, such as email, flyer on medication receipts, or telephone call, all your patients taking more than three medications to explain the medication therapy management services available at the pharmacy. This communication may include a voucher to have a free medication service assessment scheduled with the pharmacy.

> Planning entails identifying what the organization expects to accomplish, and how.

4. Define the organization's objectives. Objectives are statements of specific tasks or tactics that must be accomplished in the next one to five years for the organization to meet its goals. These tasks must specify, in measurable terms, what is to be accomplished, by what date, and its priority relative to other objectives. For example, building on the first goal listed under step 2, an organization's objective may be to provide billable comprehensive medication therapy management services by the end of fiscal year 2014 to 20% of the pharmacy patients who take three or more medications.

5. Develop functional plans. These are detailed specifications for how each objective will be met. To accomplish the objective described above, for example, you would develop a marketing plan, financial plan, and operational plan for providing comprehensive medication therapy management services for patients. See Chapter 5 for more information on these elements, which are also used for developing business plans. Functional plans must be evaluated continually by comparing what was planned to what has been accomplished.

Once the pharmacy's objectives and functional plans have been pinned down, you can develop the pharmacy's operating budget, as outlined in the box on page 118.

Basic Steps in Preparing a Pharmacy Operating Budget

Here are the basic steps in preparing an operating budget for a pharmacy. Larger organizations would follow the same steps to develop budgets for each operating unit. The operating budget illustrates the planned revenues and expenses for a future period of time. Budgeting is an iterative process that may take several "runs" to finalize. It is advisable for pharmacy managers to consult with other professionals when developing budgets, such as accountants and human resources managers, to ensure that all attributable aspects necessary for an accurate budget are captured.

1. Determine the pharmacy's objectives for the coming year. An objective would include a targeted net income. (See step 4 on page 117.)

2. Identify the programs and activities that are required to attain the pharmacy's objectives, which is part of developing functional plans for the pharmacy (step 5 on page 117).

3. Develop the revenue and expense budgets, which are based on the initial forecast of revenues and the expenses required to generate those revenues.

   • The revenue budget is based on a compilation of data including management's assumptions about business conditions, government regulations, area prescriber and consumer response to health care issues, and competition in the area.

   • The expense budget is based on assumptions or actual data regarding costs, wages, and employee productivity.

4. Determine whether the projected revenue and expenses will produce the target income.

5. If the projected revenue and expenses will not produce the target income, you must review and revise each item in the revenue and expense budgets. For example, you might determine that the personnel budget (under the expense budget) has to be reduced to meet the operational budget. This may result in yearly raises not being as high as in the past or having to hire a staff member at a lower salary.

6. Repeat step 5 until the projected revenue and expenses will produce the target income.

Source: Adapted from Budgeting. In: Carroll NV, ed. *Financial Management for Pharmacists: A Decision-Making Approach.* 3rd ed. Baltimore: Lippincott Williams & Wilkins; 2007:77–97.

Managing Expenses

Budgets are estimates. You must develop them based on solid facts, measurements, and projections, adhere to them as closely as possible, and evaluate them on a periodic basis, such as weekly or monthly. Budgets are typically monitored by using computer software programs that can account for what has been spent for each budgeted item.

Meeting budgets often depends on managing controllable expenses. In pharmacy practice settings, payroll tends to be the most controllable expense, given that most pharmacies are in charge of budgeting and allocating hours for pharmacists, pharmacy technicians, and other pharmacy support personnel.[2] Therefore, making the most of the knowledge, skills, and contributions of the pharmacist and pharmacy staff should always be a pharmacy goal so you can sustain and increase revenue, retain good employees, and have enough money to be able to fill vacancies when they occur.

Craig Long, PharmD
Pharmacy Supervisor
Kaiser Permanente

Q: What is your professional pharmacy background?

I have been a pharmacy supervisor at the Kaiser Permanente in Severna Park, Maryland, for a little over two years. My current practice setting is located in an ambulatory care medical office building. I have been a pharmacy manager in some form for the last four years.

I received my PharmD from the University of Maryland School of Pharmacy in 2004. I began my career as a pharmacist with CVS/pharmacy in Annapolis, Maryland, and three years later became a pharmacy manager at a CVS/pharmacy in Severn, Maryland. I took my current position with Kaiser Permanente in 2009. I am also a pharmacy preceptor for several pharmacy schools and two pharmacy technician programs.

Q: Please share advice for those interested in advancing to the role of pharmacy manager.

Work on building your leadership skills. Being a pharmacy manager is about not only managing your pharmacy, but also leading a team and developing those team members. Your goal as pharmacy manager should be to get your pharmacy and your employees to succeed.

Q: What most prepared you to be a pharmacy manager?
Working at CVS and being the only pharmacist on duty. When you are the only pharmacist working, you are the manager at that time. Pharmacy decisions, staffing decisions, and business decisions are your responsibility. You learn how to be an effective leader and put your team into positions where they will perform their best.

Q: Describe your biggest challenge when you first became a pharmacy manager.

It was learning how to balance being a pharmacist and a manager. Most pharmacy managers are still staff pharmacists who work side-by-side with technicians, and it can be hard to step out of the staff pharmacist role to be the leader and boss. Becoming comfortable with enforcing rules and disciplining employees while also working with them in a close environment takes practice.

Q: What have you learned from being a pharmacy manager?

I've gained many great tools that have built my career, such as how to:

- Deal with conflict and constructively discipline an employee.

- Balance everyday work with long-term goals and business objectives.

- See the other side of a business and make business decisions.

- Take criticism and learn from my management mistakes.

Part of being a good leader is not only recognizing when you have made a mistake, but also taking steps to fix it. One of the greatest parts of being a manager is seeing your team develop into a strong cohesive group and seeing your goals and objectives being met.

Q: What's your view of the value of networking and having mentors?

Pharmacy is a very small world. Networking and keeping in contact with others brings you opportunities. You never know when someone will present you with a new challenge that will better your career.

Having mentors is a fantastic way to bounce ideas off someone and learn how to become a better leader. Mentors can provide advice as you build your experience and they can guide you in the right direction. It's okay to ask questions and admit that you need help with something.

Q: What are the attributes of a good leader? A good manager?

A good leader should be honest, open minded, objective, organized, and a good listener who takes suggestions from employees. Your team is more likely to be interested in a goal or project if they feel like they had a part in creating the plan to reach that goal or complete that project.

Good managers look to the future, have a big picture in mind of where their team should go, and know how to build trust so the team will want to follow them. You must be honest and be a good role model; you must act the way you want your employees to act.

Eileen E. Munch, PharmD

**Manager of Professional and College Relations
CVS/Caremark**

Q: Tell us about your pharmacy background.

I am a 2001 graduate of Butler University College of Pharmacy and Health Sciences in Indianapolis. Upon graduation, I practiced as a clinical staff pharmacist for two years in hospitals in Florida and Illinois, in both central and decentralized staffing settings. Then in 2003 I had the opportunity to move and work for Osco Drug in the Arizona market, where I practiced as pharmacy manager and diabetes educator. In 2006, Osco Drug was acquired by CVS/pharmacy, and I transitioned to Baltimore, Maryland. For CVS I served as staff pharmacist and pharmacy team leader, and thanks to my continued focus and drive, I was promoted to pharmacy supervisor in 2008. In April 2010 I was promoted to my current position for the central Pennsylvania, eastern West Virginia, Delaware, Maryland, Virginia, and Washington, DC, areas. My professional affiliations include Phi Lambda Sigma, Phi Delta Chi, and the Maryland Pharmacists Association, and I'm a member of the Maryland Medicaid Drug Utilization Review Board.

Q: What advice would you give to a student pharmacist or staff pharmacist who seeks to become a pharmacy manager?
Never give up! If your true desire is pharmacy management, be confident, determined, and focused on your goal. Despite challenges along the way, be open to feedback and learn from those who are or have been in management positions.

Q: What prepared you to take a pharmacy manager position?

Taking advantage of knowledge and advice from other managers helped a great deal, as did working in different pharmacy practice settings with pharmacists who have different management styles.

Q: What challenges do new pharmacy managers face?

Typical challenges include time management and prioritizing, which normally are easy to overcome. The biggest challenge tends to be people management. A large part of any manager's position is building relationships with your team, managing employees' needs and concerns, keeping the team engaged, and simultaneously driving results.

Q: What benefits and rewards have you experienced as a new pharmacy manager?

One of the biggest rewards has been working with team members, helping them develop, and witnessing their growth and success. You can have a huge influence on individuals as a manager, which is a great honor.

Q: What role has networking, having a mentor, and involvement in professional associations had in your development as a pharmacy manager?

Being a part of professional organizations and acting as a preceptor for pharmacy students have allowed me to meet other pharmacy managers and pharmacists who play different roles within the realm of pharmacy. It is important to always keep lines of communication open and to share knowledge and insights with other leaders.

Q: From your perspective, what are the attributes of effective managers and leaders?

Effective managers are problem solvers. They are strategic and task-oriented and able to lead by example. Attributes of a true leader include being a visionary who is goal-driven, has high energy, is enthusiastic, and is able to value team diversity.

Exercise 4-1 | Practice Site Financial Reports

Complete this chart to describe the type(s) of financial report(s) accessible for your pharmacy practice site.				
Report Type	**Is the report available?**		**How often the report is available**	**Process to obtain report or elements related to the report**
	Yes	**No**		
Balance Sheet				
Income Statement				
Operating Budget				
Statement of Cash Flow				
Statement of Retained Earnings				
Other pharmacy financial reports:				

Additional Resources

- **Budget Choice: Planning Versus Control.** Churchill NC. *Harvard Business Rev.* 1984;62:150–64. This reference discusses the importance of both planning and control in preparing and evaluating budgets in organizations.

- **Budgeting and Financial Reporting.** Buchanan C. *Topics Hosp Pharm Manage.* 1986;63:29–52. This reference applies theories of budgeting and financial reporting in the hospital/health-system pharmacy practice settings.

- *Essentials of Managerial Finance.* 13th ed. Besley S, Brigham EF. Mason, Ohio: Thomson South-Western; 2005. This textbook discusses the basic financial management tools necessary for achieving business success. Because it applies financial theories in a practical way, the book is understandable and germane to all business settings.

- **NCPA Digest.** National Community Pharmacists Association, Alexandria, Va. Available at http://www.ncpanet.org/digestpublic/digest.php. Accessed March 17, 2011. This publication covers financial and budgeting information related to independent pharmacy practice in the United States.

References

1. Wild JJ, Larson KD, Chiappetta B. *Fundamental Accounting Principles*. 18th ed. United States: McGraw Hill Higher Education; 2007.

2. Herist KN, Wade WE. Cents and sensibility: Understanding the numbers. In: Chisholm-Burns MA, Vaillancourt AM, Shepherd M, eds. *Pharmacy Management, Leadership, Marketing, and Finance*. Sudbury, Mass: Jones and Bartlett; 2010:187–214.

3. Mosavin R. Financial reports. In: Desselle SP, Zgarrick DP, eds. *Pharmacy Management: Essentials for All Practice Settings*. United States: McGraw-Hill Companies; 2009:247–63.

4. Financial Statement Analysis. In: Carroll NV, ed. *Financial Management for Pharmacists: A Decision-Making Approach*. 3rd ed. Baltimore: Lippincott Williams & Wilkins; 2007:53–71.

5. National Centers for Disease Control and Prevention National Center for Health Statistics: Data & Statistics. Available at http://www.cdc.gov/DataStatistics. Accessed April 25, 2011.

6. Medco Drug Trend Report. Available at *http://medco.mediaroom.com/index.php?s=64&cat=5*. Accessed April 25, 2011.

7. Pedersen CA, Schneider PJ, Scheckelhoff DJ. ASHP national survey of pharmacy practice in hospital settings: Dispensing and administration 2008. *Am J Health Syst Pharm*. 2009;66:926–46.

8. Budgeting. In: Carroll NV, ed. *Financial Management for Pharmacists: A Decision-Making Approach*. 3rd ed. Baltimore: Lippincott Williams & Wilkins; 2007:77–97.

Business Plan Essentials

Why Create a Business Plan?

At some point, you may want to embark on a new initiative or enhance a current program in the pharmacy. No matter how innovative or tried-and-true the concept, you need to develop a business plan to explore the concept's viability and clarify your strategy.

A thorough business plan is a pharmacy manager's most effective tool for reaching long-term goals and achieving success with a new business, program, or service. A well-constructed plan not only describes the idea in a compelling and convincing manner, but also demonstrates that the professional abilities and business competencies are present to make the concept a reality.

Pharmacy managers must know the basics of developing an effective business plan for new programs and services. This chapter covers:

- The importance of a business plan

- Details about preparing the plan's sections

- Reviewing the business plan

You may seek multiple outcomes for your new service, such as:

- Improving patient health outcomes.

- Increasing pharmacy sales.

- Expanding customer volume at the pharmacy.

A business plan is a formal document, usually 20 to 30 pages long, that communicates new ideas to stakeholders in a standardized and organized way. The business plan conveys the components of a business strategy, including the mission statement, external and internal environments, and opportunities and threats to the practice.[1]

Among the many directions that an established pharmacy business might choose to pursue—and for which it would develop a business plan—include:

- Assisted living facility and nursing home consulting.

- Collaborative practice services with other health care providers.

- Delivery of prescription medications and devices.

- Medication therapy management (MTM) services.

- Patient education sessions (group and/or individual).

- Patient management services.

- Self-care counseling.

Elements of a Business Plan

- Cover and title page
- Executive summary
- Table of contents
- Description of the business
- Description of the service
- Marketing plan
- Financial plan
- Management team
- Operations
- Appendices

Source: Adapted from McDonough R. *The Dynamics of Pharmaceutical Care: Enriching Patients' Health: Writing a Business Plan for a New Pharmacy Service.* Monograph 23. Washington, DC: American Pharmacists Association; 2007.

The Preparation Stage

Before writing any document, you must do initial legwork so you're prepared to clearly outline what you will cover. The box above lists the elements of a business plan that you must be prepared to flesh out when you sit down to write.

The Idea

A sound business plan document must be based on a sound idea. So a major part of preparing for writing a business plan is developing the idea, service, or business that the plan will address. A business idea can be generated from many sources, including previous experiences, observations, and identified needs. For example, a pharmacy that serves a high number of patients with diabetes may find it beneficial to develop MTM services to help these patients with their diabetes and other disease states. Or it may be useful to launch patient education classes focused on diabetes management—including cooking, exercise, and medications.

Mission Statement

After you formulate the business idea, you need to develop a concise, clearly written mission statement that describes the business or practice, outlines what the business intends to accomplish, and defines the audience that the business is targeted for.[2] New pharmacy services that are developed in existing businesses should each have their own mission statement that is consistent with the overall mission statement of the business. The following elements should be contained in a mission statement:[2]

- **Intended customers.** What groups of patients or customers are likely to use the business or service?

- **Core values.** What professional values will guide the interactions or ventures with patients and other health care providers?

- **Services and products.** What kinds of services and products will the business provide?

- **Goals and philosophy.** What specific objectives are to be achieved? What benefits will patients gain from using the business or service?

- **Desired public image.** How do you want the public to perceive the service?

Writing the Business Plan

Before actually writing, it's important to gather facts about the need for the business or service you intend to launch. These facts support the rationale for the service and add strength to the business plan.

> A thorough business plan is an effective tool for achieving success with a new program or service.

You can find facts for your business plan in journal articles, on websites, and in other professional, business, and government sources. For example, in order to develop MTM services for diabetes patients, you would look into published literature, information provided by professional pharmacy organizations, and information from other medication services for patients with diabetes and chronic diseases, as well as training, certificate programs, and tools to help prepare your staff for the proposed services.

Personal communications with other people running businesses or services similar to the one you are exploring may also be useful. For example, you could contact authors of articles or other experts to ask questions, such as:

- What steps did you follow to start your service?

- Where did you find funding to initiate and sustain the service?

- What challenges did you encounter during the proposal and implementation stages?

- What advice can you give me about launching a similar service?

You could also ask these colleagues if they are willing to review part or all of your business plan. Most people who have embarked on new or expanded pharmacy services are willing to help do the same, in the spirit of improving patient care.

Cover and Title Page

On the title page, list the name of the proposed business or service as well as the contact information for the people responsible for the business plan's elements. The business plan authors should also be included.

Executive Summary

The executive summary is an abbreviated version of the business plan. It highlights the main points in the plan, summarizes the key objectives of the business or service, and explains the financial and other goals. This section should be written after all other elements of the business plan have been fully developed. In fact, the executive summary will likely be the very last piece that you write, even though it appears near the beginning of the business plan.

Description of the Business

In the business description you explain the history of the need for the new service, giving the reader sufficient background to understand how it will fit into the current environment. Relevant information may include sales, customer base, size, and scope of services for similar efforts in the geographic area, along with data on the need for the service. Your goal is to build a business case that explains why the service is needed—is there an implied demand for it, and no current supplier? You also want to sketch out how your service will differ from similar entities—such as reaching populations who are not being served right now or delivering benefits to patients that no one else provides.

If you have an existing business in which you intend to add a new service, this section will provide an overview of the current state of the business, including:

- The pharmacy's physical layout, location, and hours of operation.

- The number, type, and degree of training and expertise of the employees and associates needed for the new service.

- Characteristics of the products and services that will be provided.

Description of the Service

The service description provides information on how the proposed business will address the needs of the current environment or how the new service will build on the existing operations and strengths. Here, you should give a clear explanation of the business or service—what it is, how it will operate, and who will be involved—and define the milestones that will be used to measure the success of the business or service.

Marketing Plan

This section of the business plan should describe how the service will be marketed to create awareness and reach target audiences. Marketing focuses on satisfying customers' needs and wants through an exchange process; that is, customers will exchange something they value—money—for goods or services that benefit them in some way.

The marketing plan contains the market analysis and the marketing strategy.

Market Analysis

In this portion of the marketing plan, you describe the target market for the business or service and explain how the service will be different from the competition's offerings.[3] Include an analysis of the strengths and weaknesses of the business or service as they relate to the opportunities and threats in the external environment—commonly known as a "SWOT analysis." Table 5-1 gives examples of elements you might include in a SWOT analysis for a new pharmacy service. For a useful assessment form you can use to carry out a SWOT analysis, see pages 14–19 in the book *Managing the Patient-Centered Pharmacy,* which is listed in the Additional Resources at the end of this chapter.

The market analysis should also provide information about unmet health needs in the community that will be addressed by the new service, and it should identify other parties who may have an interest in the service, such as health care providers.

Marketing Strategy

The marketing strategy describes the methods you will use to promote the service to the targeted population, which includes patients and other interested parties.[3] You must identify the target market and describe the marketing mix you'll use.

Target Market

In describing the target market, you should cover:

- Market segmentation, including:

  o Geographic characteristics such as state, city, and zip code.

Table 5-1 | **Potential Elements of a SWOT Analysis for a New Pharmacy Service**

Strengths	Weaknesses
Experienced and trained pharmacy staff (certifications, specializations). Pharmacy patient loyalty. High-volume pharmacy. High percentage of pharmacy patients with third-party coverage. Collaborations with other local health providers.	Poor pharmacy workflow. Poor pharmacy layout. Lack or limited use of automation. Human resource issues (i.e., low pharmacy employee morale, pharmacy staff not embracing the new service).
Opportunities	Threats
Large population of patients with conditions that could benefit from the service. Relationships with prescribers and other health care providers and potential for collaborations.	Local competitors offering the same or similar service. No support from the pharmacy owner or upper management for the new service. Additional pharmacy colleagues are needed in order to implement the service. Limited payers to reimburse for service.

○ Demographic characteristics such as age, gender, education, and income.

○ Psychographic characteristics such as values and lifestyles.

○ Benefit characteristics; things that the service would aim to improve, such as medication adherence or improved quality of life.

• Market targeting—describing target customers that the business or service will pursue.

• Market positioning—differentiating the business or service in the patient's mind in terms of features, benefits, and prices.

Marketing Mix
Key aspects of the marketing mix to describe in your business plan include:

Product/service—the need being satisfied, the brand of the products and services provided, and the support services are needed for patient acceptance, such as delivery, financing, warranties, and guarantees.

- Promotion:

  o Advertising.

  o Selling.

  o Sales promotion.

  o Publicity targeting potential buyers, payers, and users of the products and services.

  o Potential promotional items such as samples, loyalty cards, discounts, and direct-mail flyers.

- Place—the location of the business and services and associated information, such as access, parking, security, and marketing venues, including the Internet.

- Price—the cost of the service to the target audience.

Financial Plan

The financial plan examines the revenue expected from developing and sustaining the new business or service. In this section, you describe the projected revenue from sources such as product sales, and you look at anticipated expenses, such as staff time, marketing costs, rent, utilities, and equipment. Table 5-2 gives examples of potential revenue and expenses to consider when formulating financial plans.

Table 5-2 | Revenue and Expense Projection Considerations

Revenue Projections	Expense Projections
Income from the new business/service	Start-up costs: cost of training, equipment, reconstruction, supplies.
Supplemental sales from the new business/service	Fixed costs: costs that do not change with changes in the volume of the business/service, such as rent.
Fee-based compensation from patients/customers or health insurers	Variable costs: costs that do change with changes in the volume of the business/service, such as the cost of the pharmacist professional service.

Source: Adapted from Haag AB. Writing a successful business plan. *Am Assoc Occup Health Nurses J.* 1997;45:25–32.

The financial plan should project a break-even point, which is the point in time when revenues equal expenses for the business or service. For new services in an existing pharmacy, you'll need historical and projection financial statements from the pharmacy, including the following:[4]

- Income and expense statements

- Balance sheets

- Cash flow statements

Develop the financial plan to cover the first three to five years of the new business or service.[4] Include an explanation of how the business start-up will be funded. Potential funding can come from external sources such as bank and personal loans as well as internally from the pharmacy owner.

> Before writing any document, you must do initial legwork so you're prepared to clearly outline what you will cover.

In the financial plan, include any assumptions on which the plan is based and their rationale. You may need to consult with an accountant to ensure that this section covers all the necessary information.

Finally, a contingency plan (exit strategy) should be included in the financial plan.[4] You might start with a full-service business, but as a contingency plan, you could downsize, eliminate certain services, or sell the business.

Management Team

Having an efficient and knowledgeable management team in place is essential for your new business or service to prosper. In your business plan, the management team section should explain how the qualifications and experience of the senior manager (or managers) who will oversee the service are necessary for it to be implemented successfully. The section might start with a paragraph about overall capabilities and then offer specific bullet points describing the expertise and its applicability to the service. In the business plan's appendices, you can include résumés or curricula vitae (CVs) for the management team members.

Operations

In this section of the business plan, you discuss the processes involved in delivering the service and, if applicable, explain how the service will be integrated into the existing environment or pharmacy setting. Among the key processes to discuss are:

- Staffing.

- Documentation and record keeping.

- Workflow.

- Compliance with federal and state regulations.

- Methods for feedback and evaluating the service, which may include the following—

  ○ Sales and other business metrics.

  ○ Employee feedback surveys.

  ○ Analysis of clinical outcomes.

  ○ Patient utilization and satisfaction surveys.

> A business idea can be generated from many sources, including previous experiences, observations, and identified needs.

Finally, this section should provide a timeline for the business plan. A formal business plan usually projects business operations for three years. Informal business plans can operate on a shorter time frame, depending on the needs of the managers of the business. The timeline should provide information on the tasks, people responsible for the tasks, and week/month for completing the task.

For example, for an MTM service for diabetes patients, the timeline would include:

- Researching MTM services.

- Identifying the specific MTM services to be provided.

- Determining charges for the services.

- Finding and training staff members to provide the services.

- Working out mechanisms for payment for the MTM services.

Appendices

In this section, add information and documents to supplement the business plan, such as:

- Articles justifying the service.

- Data (charts and tables) supporting the need for the service.

- Detailed financial plan information.

- Résumés or CVs for the management team.

Reviewing the Business Plan

Before the business plan is officially accepted, it should be reviewed by people who are not associated with it or its potential outcome, but who have expertise related to the section you ask them to review. Ultimately, you should have a minimum of one reviewer per section. It's also helpful if someone who has written a successful business plan can review yours for completeness and clarity.

The authors of the business plan should carefully consider all suggestions and edits provided by the reviewers. After you finish revising the content, have someone who is proficient in writing and editing check the plan for grammar and spelling. Your final business plan should be easy to read, well organized, and attractive.

Review and update the business plan annually to reflect changes in the external market or internal pharmacy operations.[5]

Meghan Sullivan, PharmD

Assistant Professor, University of New England College of Pharmacy

Q: What is your professional pharmacy background?

I received my PharmD with a minor in business from the Nesbitt College of Pharmacy at Wilkes University. Then I completed a Community Practice/Ambulatory Care Residency with The Ohio State University College of Pharmacy and Kroger Patient Care Center, Columbus, Ohio. After my residency, I was an assistant professor of pharmacy practice, with an emphasis on community pharmacy practice, at the University of Maryland School of Pharmacy, and I served as the inaugural AFPE-NACDS Foundation Pharmacy Faculty Fellow.

To fulfill my practice site responsibilities while at the University of Maryland, I served as a clinical pharmacist for a chain pharmacy. At my practice site, I was responsible for designing, developing, and implementing medication therapy management (MTM) services and community outreach events. I have received certificate training in immunizations, diabetes education, and MTM.

Q: **What advice do you have for a student or staff pharmacist who wants to become a pharmacy manager?**

Do your homework. First, you have to step back and think about your strengths, areas needing improvement, and personal and professional goals and aspirations. Seek out mentors who can provide sound guidance and advice throughout your journey.

Next, take time to learn about the qualifications and expectations of the position. Obtain the necessary tools and training to be successful in the position.

Finally, once you are in the position of pharmacy manager, ensure that everything—mission, vision, goals, and so on—is communicated clearly and that all stakeholders, including your supervisor and direct reports, see eye-to-eye on how goals will be achieved.

Q: What prepared you to take a pharmacy manager position?

My pharmacy manager position is nontraditional in that I am a clinical pharmacist with a more "behind the scenes" administrative role in designing, developing, and implementing MTM services throughout pharmacies within a chain pharmacy division. My pharmacy education and residency training most certainly played a vital role in preparing me because I was able to take an in-depth look at systematically creating such programming.

Seeking mentorship from those who've had similar positions was most beneficial. I learned very quickly that there is no need to reinvent the wheel when I can tap the experiences of others and make adjustments to suit my own needs.

It's also essential to become familiar with the resources available in your field.

Q: What challenges did you face as a new pharmacy manager?

My biggest obstacle was cultivating growth through change. I was in a unique situation because my role focused on implementing MTM services. Designing and developing programming to fit the needs of all pharmacists throughout the division was very challenging.

Having very few years of experience was difficult as well. I had to work hard to prove my worth to those skeptical of my management abilities and my plans to add a rather large expectation into their already hectic work schedule.

I learned through trial and error and built upon my experiences. I had to learn how to take chances, ask questions, seek assistance, and say "no."

Q: What benefits have you experienced as a new pharmacy manager?

Being a pharmacy manager is truly rewarding. It has given me the opportunity to work with an amazing group of pharmacists who have a wide range of training and experience. Together, we have cultivated a program that is fulfilling not only for each of us, both personally and professionally, but also for our patients. Being a trailblazer during this time of change has been an honor; I've contributed to an effort that impacts our profession, enhances pharmacists' professional satisfaction, and improves patient outcomes.

Q: What roles have networking, having a mentor, and involvement in professional associations had in your development as a pharmacy manager?

Developing the knowledge and skills to be a successful pharmacy manager is not an easy feat, and most certainly not something you can do solely on your own. Consulting with people who have prior experience in management positions is vital to ensuring stability within your position.

Through networking, you communicate with others who have been or are currently involved in a similar position. It's invaluable to strategize together and discuss triumphs and tribulations encountered along the way.

Support from mentors is a tremendous asset, especially when they help you grow both personally and professionally. In addition to guiding and supporting you, they can lead you through a decision-making process so you draw on your strengths, aspirations, and accomplishments.

You really must get involved and stay involved in local, state, and national associations. Members of these organizations form a strong support network to accomplish tasks at hand, and they're able to take advantage of resources that may not be accessible otherwise, including networking opportunities and contact with potential mentors.

Q: From your perspective, what are the attributes of a manager? Of a leader?

Successful managers and leaders know how to forge meaningful relationships with others to identify and achieve common goals. Visionaries and facilitators of change tend to thrive in leadership positions because they lead by example and empower others to be passionate about the tasks at hand.

Managers should be able to establish realistic expectations for their employees and use appropriate, fair methods for evaluation and feedback. Managers and leaders must truly listen to the ideas and concerns of those they oversee to ensure harmony among the group and maintain a supportive environment where everyone feels appreciated and part of the team.

Exercise 5-1 | Considerations for a New Pharmacy Service

Complete this chart to describe ideas and information that may be needed before you start working on a business plan.	
Issue	**Response**
Characteristics of our typical pharmacy patient: Gender: Age: Income: Disease(s): Buying Habits (aside from prescriptions):	
What are some issues that our patients/ customers/clients/health care colleagues often discuss regarding our pharmacy and its services?	
What are some areas of the pharmacy business where we can expand services for our patients/customers/clients/health care colleagues?	
What information or data is needed to investigate potentially expanding services?	
What other stakeholders should be involved in the discussion of potentially expanding services?	
What resources (including revenue, tools, technology, expertise) are needed for the expansion of services?	
What are the opportunities and threats in the external environment for the expansion of services?	

Additional Resources

- *Anatomy of a Business Plan.* 4th ed. Pinson L, Jinnett J. Chicago: Dearborn Trade Publications; 1999. Inside this book is a step-by-step process to create well-constructed business plans and to keep the plan updated.

- **Beyond the 4Ps: Using Relationship Marketing to Build Value and Demand for Pharmacy Services.** Doucette WR, McDonough RP. *J Am Pharm Assoc.* 2002;42:183–93. This article describes how to create and maintain a network of productive relationships with selected groups of patients and stakeholders to expand pharmacy care services.

- *Center for Business Planning.* www.businessplans.org. This website provides resources for business plan development and implementation as well as samples of business plans.

- *The Entrepreneur's Guide to Writing Business Plans and Proposals.* Chambers KD. Westport, Conn: Praeger; 2008. This reference walks you through writing proposals and business plans in an effective, business-wise manner.

- *How to Develop a Business Plan for Pharmacy Services.* 2nd ed. Schumock GT, Stubbings J. Lenexa, KS: American College of Clinical Pharmacy; 2007. This book provides information on how to plan, develop, launch, and evaluate business services in the field of pharmacy.

- *Managing the Patient-Centered Pharmacy.* Hagel HP, Rovers JP, eds. Washington, DC: American Pharmacists Association; 2002. This book shares a process-oriented approach for developing a new practice or patient-care service in light of infrastructure, management, and financial considerations. Pages 14 to 19 provide a detailed worksheet for carrying out a SWOT analysis.

- **Small Business Administration Small Business Planner.** www.sba.gov/smallbusinessplanner/plan/writeabusinessplan/index.html. This website, operated by the U.S. Small Business Administration, covers all aspects of starting a business, including writing a business plan, establishing the business, finance preparation, and pertinent laws and regulations.

- *Your First Business Plan.* 2nd ed. Covello J, Hazelgren B. Naperville, Ill: Sourcebooks: 1995. Designed to help readers write their own business plan, this book uses a question-and-answer format.

References

1. McDonough R. *The Dynamics of Pharmaceutical Care: Enriching Patients' Health: Writing a Business Plan for a New Pharmacy Service.* Monograph 23. Washington, DC: American Pharmacists Association; 2007.

2. Hagel HP, Rovers JP, eds. *Managing the Patient-Centered Pharmacy.* Washington, DC: American Pharmacists Association; 2002:5–10.

3. McDonough RP, Pithan ES, Doucette WR, et al. Marketing pharmaceutical care services. *J Am Pharm Assoc.* 1998;38:667–81.

4. Haag AB. Writing a successful business plan. *Am Assoc Occup Health Nurses J.* 1997;45:25–32.

5. Pinson L, Jinnett J. *Anatomy of a Business Plan.* Chicago: Dearborn Trade Publications; 1993:30–2.

The Key Ingredient—You

Soft Skills for Solid Results

So, far, this book has discussed everything from legal considerations to human resources issues to financial responsibilities. What about those "soft skills" that help you generate the best possible results in your pharmacy setting? Books have been written by the dozens on how to manage, motivate, and help employees achieve their very best work. The following pages provide a quick snapshot of ways to build effective relationships and promote your own growth.

Build Credibility and Rapport

Pharmacy managers have a responsibility to encourage productivity and promote the organization's goals.[1] Being able to do this means building trust and rapport with pharmacy staff members. Otherwise, it's very difficult to be effective in your role. Following are some ideas for developing credibility.

Pharmacy managers need to build their interpersonal skills and promote effective relationships with others. This chapter provides tips for:

- Building trust and rapport with employees

- Maintaining effective work relationships

- Boosting your personal growth and emotional intelligence

- Being a good leader

- **Lead by example.** To bring about change and improve performance, pharmacy managers must model the behaviors they are trying to encourage. You must demonstrate competence and be willing to work steadily at a task until it is complete, and refrain from asking any member of the pharmacy team to do something that you are not willing or able to do.

- **Consider problems carefully and promptly.** Though problems require thoughtful solutions, do not delay in addressing them. Situations that are not handled as soon as feasible will fester and can lead to additional challenges.

- **Be fair and consistent.** You must remember that every action establishes a precedent, and at the same time, you must know when to be flexible. People remember the decisions made in the past and who was affected. Being fair and consistent with your actions helps you avoid being accused of favoritism.

- **Admit mistakes.** Every manager makes mistakes. Admitting them to someone, whether it's your boss, a mentor, or members of the pharmacy team, allows you to show your human side and also to learn from the situation. A mistake is not a defeat; it's an experience that leads to professional and personal growth.

- **Give direct reports as much responsibility as possible.** Once you've learned about your staff's abilities and desires, delegate tasks they are ready to handle so they can grow and you can focus on management responsibilities.

- **Give credit when it is due.** Don't be afraid to give praise often. It makes staff members feel appreciated and promotes a positive team atmosphere. A simple "thank you" can go a long way.

- **Be discreet.** Sometimes you'll need to coach and counsel team members when their performance is below par. Do so in private and keep confidential any sensitive information regarding members of your team.

- **Think of employees as customers.** In essence, employees are another segment of your customer base. Take their suggestions seriously, observe what is going on in the pharmacy setting, and practice active listening so you're on top of the team's desires and challenges. Address staff members' needs and requests as soon as you can. As much as possible, pharmacy managers should use their power and influence to benefit their team.

- **Be organized.** Keep good records and ensure that all documentation is accurate. Thoroughly prepare for all meetings and presentations and follow up on issues and promises within a reasonable time period.

Tips for Maintaining Effective Work Relationships

• Be approachable; maintain eye contact and use body language that indicates you are receptive to other people.

• Resolve challenges using a mutual problem-solving approach, if possible. Work cooperatively with direct reports to identify the root cause of issues and potential solutions.

• Accept people as they are. You can't change people's personalities, but you can give them responsibilities that accentuate their strengths and offer professional development opportunities to help them build skills they don't feel comfortable with.

• Be open-minded.

• Keep personal feelings out of business decisions.

• Use active listening to inquire, listen, and understand other people. Give the speaker your full attention and paraphrase at times to ensure you are grasping the message.

• Consult with others before deciding on a final action.

• Consider difficult behavior a joint challenge. The manager must identify it and convey to the employee why it is unacceptable, and the employee must work on improving the behavior—with guidance from the manager.

• Don't avoid conflicts; instead, manage them to bring about positive outcomes. Conflicts do not go away if a manager ignores them; if anything, they fester and ultimately affect some aspect of your business.

• Work in the present. Be attentive to what is going on now and don't reference past mistakes or instances in which directions were not followed. Once a problem has been resolved, don't keep bringing it up.

• **Have fun at work and at home.** We spend many more hours at work with colleagues than we do at home with our family and friends—so it's important to have a work environment that is not only productive, but also enjoyable. Fun at work can include small things, such as:

  ○ Recognizing an employee of the month.

○ Celebrating birthdays and other occasions.

○ Holding events outside the pharmacy, such as bowling night.

○ Launching special competitions for pharmacy team members and offering small prizes or incentives for the winners.

Being an effective manager is as much about maintaining effective work relationships as it is about building them. The box on page 147 suggests things you can do to maintain effective relationships at work.

Work on Personal Growth and Emotional Intelligence

Emotional intelligence is a key contributor to individual growth.

As you progress in your role as a pharmacy manager, you will grow both personally and professionally. A key contributor to individual growth is emotional intelligence, or "EI," a term that entered everyday vocabulary after psychologist and *New York Times* reporter Daniel Goleman published his bestseller *Emotional Intelligence* in 1995. Emotional intelligence has many definitions, including, as Goleman puts it, "the capacity for recognizing our own feelings and those of others, for motivating ourselves, and for managing emotions well in ourselves and our relationships."[2]

One EI model, the mixed effects model, focuses on a wide array of competencies and skills that determine leadership performance and includes the following components:[3]

1. **Self-awareness.** The ability to read one's emotions and recognize their impact while using "gut feelings" to guide decisions.

2. **Self-management.** Involves controlling one's emotions and impulses and adapting to changing circumstances.

3. **Social awareness.** The ability to sense, understand, and react to others' emotions while comprehending social networks.

4. **Relationship management.** The ability to inspire, influence, and develop others while managing conflict.

EI helps you create and sustain interpersonal relationships and effectiveness in the workplace. Some tips for maximizing your EI include:

- Be aware of your emotions and how they affect your interactions with others.

- Recognize and ask others how you react to stressful situations.

- Stay calm and in control in difficult situations, including conflicts.

- Be cognizant of how your actions or inactions affect others.

- Take responsibility for your actions and apologize when necessary, even if it is some time after the incident or confrontation.

In addition to building your EI, additional measures you can take to boost your personal development include:

- **Strive to communicate effectively.** Use clear, precise verbal and written communication and know how to listen closely, execute meetings and meet their objectives, make presentations, negotiate, and speak effectively in public.

- **Be a continuous learner.** Seek out programs and initiatives to expand your current knowledge and to build a knowledge base in new areas. These initiatives can be informal, such as observational visits to other pharmacies, and formal, such as live or online management courses.

- **Work on improving your leadership.** Areas to focus on include the following:

  ○ Caring—demonstrating the ability to empathize with other people's needs, concerns, and goals.

  ○ Being comfortable with ambiguity, which involves taking calculated risks, handling a certain level of disruption and conflict, and being willing to change perspective when new information comes to light.

  ○ Persistence—maintaining a positive, focused attitude in pursuing a goal, despite the obstacles.

○ Political astuteness—acquiring a solid sense of your organization's power structure, listening attentively to the concerns of its most powerful groups, and knowing where to turn for needed support and resources.

○ Maintaining a level head in the midst of turmoil and confusion.

○ Self-awareness—knowing how your own patterns of behavior impact others in your practice and organization.

○ Being future-focused—understanding how your practice fits into the larger organization and society as well as how to organize short-term tasks according to long-term priorities.

• **Seek out a mentor or confidant.** Find someone you can rely on to give you honest feedback on how you are progressing and suggestions for additional training and development.

Face It: You're a Leader!

Whether you realize it or not, when you're a pharmacy manager, you become a leader. Others will look up to you and rely on you—and you will set the example and tone for those in your department. The sidebar at right summarizes the characteristics of a leader.

Throughout your career as a pharmacy manager you'll need to continue developing your interpersonal skills and nurturing the growth of others. Best of luck as you take the tips outlined in this book and make your aspirations a reality.

Leadership Characteristics

• Trustworthy
• Consistent
• Honest
• Confident
• Knowledgeable
• Goal-oriented
• Positive attitude
• Dedicated
• Enthusiastic
• Calming
• Committed to excellence
• Visionary
• Provides regular feedback/evaluations
• Supportive through difficult changes
• Recognizes staff efforts
• Takes control of difficult situations
• Plans and delegates
• Engaged at work and during conversations

Source: Adapted from Kotter JP. *What Leaders Really Do.* Harvard Business Review OnPoint Enhanced Edition. Boston: Harvard Business School Publishing; 2000.

Janet Teeters, RPh, MS

Director of Accreditation Services
American Society of Health-System
Pharmacists (ASHP)

Q: Talk a little about your professional background.

In my position at ASHP, I am in charge of the process for accrediting pharmacy residency and technician training programs across the United States. Working with the ASHP Commission on Credentialing, we accredit over 1250 pharmacy residency programs and 170 technician training programs. Since 2002, when I started in this position, our volume has more than doubled, and it looks like it will only continue to grow.

I received a BS in pharmacy from the University of Wisconsin School of Pharmacy and spent four years as a pharmacist in a clinic and small hospital in northern Wisconsin. Then I went on to complete a two-year combined master's degree and ASHP-accredited residency in hospital pharmacy at the University of Minnesota Hospital and Clinics. As a manager, I went from inpatient supervisor at the Veterans Administration System in Philadelphia to assistant director of operations at New England Medical Center in Boston.

When my husband's career moved us to Chicago, I became assistant director at Lutheran General Hospital (LGH) in Park Ridge, Illinois, and within a year I became the director of pharmacy, a position I held for 13 years. During that time I also became director of rehabilitation services at LGH and then was appointed director of pharmacy for Advocate Health Care, an integrated health system in the Chicago area that included nine hospitals at the time, one of which was LGH.

I've always been active in professional pharmacy organizations. I served as president of the New England Council of Hospital Pharmacists and the Illinois Council of Health-System Pharmacists. I also attended the Duke University Hospital Pharmacy Development Institute at the Fuqua School of Business, as well as the Northwestern University Executive Development Program at the Kellogg Graduate School of Management.

Q: What's your advice for becoming a pharmacy manager?

- **Let your aspirations be known.** Make sure others know you are interested in management and volunteer to be involved in committees within your company and in professional organizations. Managers and leaders like to mentor individuals interested in management and leadership. There is much you can learn from others as you take part in committees and group projects.

- **Stay well connected professionally.** Networking with managers inside and outside the profession can help you keep up with the latest trends, open opportunities (jobs, presentations, publishing, research), and provide a good sounding board when you have questions or concerns.

- **Seek extra training to expand your management horizons.** Look at residency programs in health-system administration, advanced management training (MS, MBA, or MPH), or special programs provided by professional organizations, such as week-long immersion programs or year-long programs like the ASHP Foundation Pharmacy Leadership Academy.

- **Always continue to learn.** Keep up with trends in leadership and management as well as changes in the profession. Learn from your mistakes, admit them, and think of them as opportunities to grow professionally.

- **Keep the patient's needs first.** You can hardly go wrong when decisions are always focused on the needs of your patients.

Q: What prepared you for pharmacy management?

I was very fortunate to enter a combined pharmacy residency/MS program with great instructors, preceptors, and mentors, whose teachings and advice gave me an excellent foundation for moving into pharmacy management. I have stayed connected with several of these individuals throughout my career.

From my student days to the present, I've always been active in professional pharmacy organizations, which has given me a great network of people to learn from and many opportunities to attend educational sessions to advance my knowledge and skills.

Q: What challenges did you face as a new pharmacy manager?

When you become a manager, it changes your relationship with staff. You need to be extremely fair, open minded, and careful not to show favoritism or biases. By helping each staff member be successful, you determine the success of your department and the organization. It's challenging at first to move from being good friends to being a good boss.

As you take on more advanced management positions, such as director, you realize "the buck stops with you." I became extremely cautious and thorough, asking many questions and trying to ensure the best results from processes our department was implementing. No matter how safe you consider the processes you have built, or how much training you've provided your staff, you realize that significant errors can occur. The first time you have to walk up to a family member and explain how an error happened that harmed their loved one, it's extremely difficult. You need to have a great deal of empathy to be a successful manager or leader, especially during times like that. So you really must learn about emotional intelligence to be successful.

Q: What benefits and rewards have you gained as a pharmacy manager?

My job is never boring. I see challenges and opportunities to tackle every day. No two days are ever alike, and if you like solving mysteries and making changes, then management is an excellent career for you.

It's extremely rewarding to implement new services that make a difference in a patient's quality of life. To start from a concept and take it through approval to successful implementation is gratifying. It's also great to see individuals you have mentored go on to be successful and make an impact in the profession. You can make a difference in the profession, even if it takes a while. Perseverance is a great trait to have in management.

Q: What roles have networking, mentors, and professional associations had in your development as a pharmacy manager?

I discovered all of my pharmacy jobs through networking while involved in professional associations. Several times I was sought out for positions based on contacts I made through my professional association work. I guess it is fitting that now I give back to the profession by being employed at a professional association that helps ensure quality training.

The continuing education programs, networking, and committee work I took part in at professional meetings were key to my success as a manager. It is impossible for me to imagine managers who can be extremely successful and enjoy their job without this level of engagement in the profession.

I have had many mentors throughout my career, and I stay connected with them to discuss challenges and opportunities. It's nice to know they are always there to listen and provide advice or direction.

Q: What are the attributes of a manager? Of a leader?

I see a good manager as extremely fair, always trying to understand all sides of an issue. Good managers are reliable, thorough in investigating each situation, generous in helping individual staff members be successful, and committed to delivering quality results on time.

True leaders are passionate about their mission and profession. They are a champion for causes, can paint a clear vision, and typically are persistent, confident, and articulate. If you have ever worked with a good leader, you just want to follow and make the vision or mission succeed, because you believe in the leader and you want to be part of the vision's success. An excellent leader also values and respects you and encourages you to help meet the vision—which makes you want to follow the leader all the more.

Exercise 6-1 | Online Emotional Intelligence Test

Take 35 minutes to complete the free online Emotional Intelligence Test at Queendom.com found at http://www.queendom.com/tests/access_page/index.htm?idRegTest=1121. Afterwards, record the following:
Current Emotional Intelligence rating:
Area(s) that indicate strong emotional intelligence:
Area(s) of emotional intelligence that can be worked on:

Additional Resources

- **Change Management Learning Center:** www.change-management.com. This website provides information on training and resources to help people and companies lead effective change in management, strategy, and other aspects of business.

- *The Heart of Leadership: 12 Practices of Courageous Leaders.* Staub II, RE. Provo, Utah: Executive Excellence Publishing; 1996. This reference describes a dozen essential elements to strengthen leadership abilities and execution.

- *Leadership Transitions.* Boston: Harvard Business School Publishing; 2001. In this program, newly promoted managers and others receive tools, tips, and resources that address transitioning in new leadership roles, including an overall topic overview, assessment, and instructions for planning and tracking progress.

- *Primal Leadership: Realizing the Power of Emotional Intelligence.* Goleman D, Boyatzis R, McKee A. Boston: Harvard Business School Press; 2002. This book makes the case for building emotional intelligence in leaders and discusses the importance of developing "resonant leadership" that demonstrates the role of the four competencies of emotional intelligence.

- *Results-Based Leadership.* Ulrich D, Zenger J, Smallwood N. Harvard Business School Press; 1999. This reference describes the leadership priorities of four areas of a company (employees, organization, customers, and investors) and ways members of management can focus on and prioritize these areas as well as deal effectively with the challenges associated with them.

- *What Makes a Leader?* Goleman D. Harvard Business Review OnPoint Enhanced Edition, February 2000. This reference discusses the five components of emotional intelligence: self-awareness, self-regulation, motivation, empathy, and social skill.

References

1. Wick J. Supervision of pharmacy personnel. *J Am Pharm Assoc.* 1998;38(4):457–68.

2. Goleman D. *Emotional Intelligence: Why It Can Matter More Than IQ.* New York: Bantam Books; 1995:4–5.

3. Goleman D. *Working with Emotional Intelligence.* New York: Bantam Books; 1998:49–70.

Index

Note: Page numbers followed by f and t indicate figures and tables, respectively.

A

AACP. *See* American Association of Colleges of Pharmacy
AAPS. *See* American Association of Pharmaceutical Scientists
AAPT. *See* American Association of Pharmacy Technicians
ACA. *See* American College of Apothecaries
Academy of Managed Care Pharmacy (AMCP), 55t
accent, and communication, 19t
accommodation, in conflict management, 86t
accounting, 103–110
    basic principles of, 104
    financial statements in, 104–108, 124
    ratio analysis in, 108, 109t
accounts payable, 105
accounts receivable, 105
ACCP. *See* American College of Clinical Pharmacy
Accreditation Council for Pharmacy Education (ACPE), 70
accuracy, in feedback for employees, 84
ACPE. *See* Accreditation Council for Pharmacy Education
administrator, 3, 3f, 4t
advanced pharmacy practice experiences (APPEs), 70, 71t
advice
    from Brandt, 92
    from Ellsworth, 20
    from Israbian-Jamgochian, 60–61
    from Leikach, 23
    from Long, 120
    from Munch, 122
    from Shimoda, 58–59
    from Sullivan, 138
    from Summerfield, 94–95
    from Teeters, 152
Age Discrimination in Employment Act of 1967 (ADEA), 33t
agenda, setting of, 5–6
alliances, value of, 7
AMCP. *See* Academy of Managed Care Pharmacy

C

D

F

G

H

Haight Act of 2008, 46
harassment, sexual, 36
hard-skill training, 78
headhunters (search firms), 75
Health Insurance Portability and Accountability Act (HIPAA) of 1996, 39–43
  covered entities under, 39, 40, 41
  employer's requirements on, 64
  minimum necessary standard of, 41
  overview of, website for, 39
  patient pharmacy rights under, 42t
  penalties for violations of, 43
  personnel training on, 42–43, 78
  pharmacies and, 41–42, 43t–45t
  provisions of, 39
  terms related to, definitions of, 40–41
HIPAA. See Health Insurance Portability and Accountability Act of 1996
hiring process, 73–79
  colleagues and staff involved in, 74
  defining position requirements in, 74
  effectiveness of, evaluating, 78–79
  employment offer in, 76, 77f
  evaluating staffing needs in, 74
  orientation in, 78, 97–98
  screening and evaluation in, 75–76
  sourcing strategy for, 75
  steps in, 73
hostile work environment harassment, 36
human resource management, 73–88
  coaching and counseling in, 78, 83–84
  conflict resolution in, 85–88
  delegating in, 81, 81t–82t
  hiring process in, 73–79
  motivating personnel in, 79–80, 98
  resources on, 100–101

I

IACP. See International Academy of Compounding Pharmacists
idea, for business plan, 129, 141
immediate dismissal, of employee, 89
income, net, 107
income statement, 104, 106–108, 124, 135
  basic equation of, 106
  expenses in, 106–107, 107t
  revenue in, 106
intelligence, emotional. See emotional intelligence
interdependence conflicts, 85

internal theft, 112
International Academy of Compounding Pharmacists (IACP), 56*t*
Internet pharmacies, regulation of, 46
internships, 69
interviews, in hiring process, 75–76
introductory pharmacy practice experiences (IPPEs), 70, 71*t*
inventory, 110–112
    assigning cost in, 111
    control of, 110
    general guidelines for managing, 113
    loss of controlled substances in, 47–48
    measurement of, 110–112
    periodic system of, 110–111
    perpetual system of, 110–111
    shrink in, 112
IPPEs. *See* introductory pharmacy practice experiences
Israbian-Jamgochian, Lenna, 60–62

J

job description
    creating, in hiring process, 74
    for pharmacy manager, 1, 2*f*
job performance
    coaching and counseling on, 83–84
    definition of, 79
    evaluation of, 78–79
    feedback on, 84
    motivation and, 79–80, 98
    termination for lack of, 88–89, 90*t*

L

laissez-faire managerial style, 10*t*
law. *See also specific laws*
    controlled substances, 46–48
    employment, 31, 32*t*–35*t*
    privacy and confidentiality, 39–43
    resources on, 65
    sexual harassment, 36
leadership, 5–11
    accepting role of, 150
    adapting style of, 27–28
    in agenda setting, 5–6
    Brandt on, 93
    characteristics of, 150
    conflicting styles of, 85
    in conflict management, 87–88
    continua of, 8–9, 8*f*, 9*t*

M

S

T